Teacher's Program Overview

Authors

Randall I. Charles
Professor Emeritus
Department of Mathematics
San Jose State University
San Jose, California

Janet H. Caldwell
Professor of Mathematics
Rowan University
Glassboro, New Jersey

Mary Cavanagh
Executive Director of Center for Practice, Research,
and Innovation in Mathematics Education (PRIME)
Arizona State University
Mesa, Arizona

Juanita Copley
Professor Emerita, College of Education
University of Houston
Houston, Texas

Warren D. Crown
Professor Emeritus of Mathematics Education
Graduate School of Education
Rutgers University
New Brunswick, New Jersey

Francis (Skip) Fennell
L. Stanley Bowlsbey Professor of Education and
Graduate and Professional Studies
McDaniel College
Westminster, Maryland

Stuart J. Murphy
Visual Learning Specialist
Boston, Massachusetts

Kay B. Sammons
Coordinator of Elementary Mathematics
Howard County Public Schools
Ellicott City, Maryland

Jane F. Schielack
Professor of Mathematics
Associate Dean for Assessment and Pre K–12
Education, College of Science
Texas A&M University
College Station, Texas

William F. Tate IV
Edward Mallinckrodt Distinguished University
Professor in Arts & Sciences
Washington University
St. Louis, Missouri

Scott Foresman·Addison Wesley

Common Core

PEARSON

Glenview, Illinois • Boston, Massachusetts • Chandler, Arizona • Upper Saddle River, New Jersey

Consulting Author

Grant Wiggins
Researcher and Educational Consultant
Hopewell, New Jersey

Mathematicians

David M. Bressoud
DeWitt Wallace Professor of
Mathematics
Macalester College
St. Paul, Minnesota

Roger Howe
Professor of Mathematics
Yale University
New Haven, Connecticut

Gary Lippman
Professor of Mathematics and Computer
Science
California State University East Bay
Hayward, California

ELL Consultant

Jim Cummins
Professor
The University of Toronto
Toronto, Canada

Common Core State Standards Reviewers

Elizabeth Baker
Mathematics Coordinator
Gilbert Public Schools
Gilbert, Arizona

Amy Barber
K–12 Math Coach
Peninsula School District ESC
Gig Harbor, Washington

Laura Cua
Teacher
Columbus City Schools
Columbus, Ohio

Wafa Deeb-Westervelt
Assistant Superintendent for Curriculum,
Instruction, and Professional
Development
Freeport Public Schools
Freeport, New York

Lynn Gullette
Title 1 Math Intervention
Mobile County Public Schools
Gilliard Elementary
Mobile, Alabama

Beverly K. Kimes
Director of Mathematics
Birmingham City Schools
Birmingham, Alabama

Kelly O'Rourke
Elementary School Assistant Principal
Clark County School District
Las Vegas, Nevada

Piper L. Riddle
Evidence-Based Learning Specialist
Canyons School District
Sandy, Utah

Debra L. Vitale
Math Coach
Bristol Public Schools
Bristol, Connecticut

Diane T. Wehby
Math Support Teacher
Birmingham City Schools
Birmingham, Alabama

ISBN-13: 978-0-328-67270-7
ISBN-10: 0-328-67270-X

2 3 4 5 6 7 8 9 10 V003 15 14 13 12 11

Contents

Content Guide

Program Guide

About the Authors

Randall I. Charles
Professor Emeritus
    Department of Mathematics
San Jose State University
San Jose, California

Randall Charles has teaching experience at all levels, and was a K–12 mathematics supervisor for five years. He is the former Vice President of the National Council of Supervisors of Mathematics. He was a member of the NCTM Research Advisory Committee, and has authored or edited many publications for NCTM. He was a member of the writing team for the NCTM Curriculum Focal Points.

Much of Randy's writing and research have focused on problem solving. He was the senior author on a widely-used series called *Problem Solving Experiences in Mathematics*. He is a senior author with Pearson Scott Foresman and Pearson Prentice Hall where he has authored more than 100 textbooks for grades K–college.

Janet H. Caldwell
Professor of Mathematics
Rowan University
Glassboro, New Jersey

Janet Caldwell teaches mathematics and directs projects providing professional development to teachers of mathematics. She has received a Professor of the Year Award and a Distinguished Teaching Award.

Mary Cavanagh
Executive Director of Center for
    Practice, Research, and Innovation
    in Mathematics Education (PRIME)
Arizona State University
Mesa, Arizona

Mary Cavanagh works with English language learners, their families, and teachers. Her most recent work includes developing a model math and science curriculum and professional development for after-school programs.

Stuart J. Murphy
Visual Learning Specialist
Boston, Massachusetts

Stuart Murphy works in the field of visual learning and is the author of the 63-book *MathStart* series. He is part of the authorship team of the Pearson Prentice Hall High School mathematics program and *digits*, Pearson Education's new Middle Grades mathematics program. He is also the author of *I SEE I LEARN*, a series of storybooks for Pre-Kindergarten children.

Kay B. Sammons
Coordinator of Elementary
    Mathematics
Howard County Public Schools
Ellicott City, Maryland

Kay Sammons is responsible for development of curriculum and assessment. She provides professional development for teachers in the areas of curriculum implementation, pedagogy, assessment, and intervention.

Juanita V. Copley
Professor Emerita
    College of Education
University of Houston
Houston, Texas

Nita Copley researches
professional development
models for early childhood
teachers and young
children's understanding
of mathematical concepts,
especially word problems and
problem-solving strategies.

Warren D. Crown
Professor Emeritus of
    Mathematics Education
Graduate School of Education
Rutgers University
New Brunswick, New Jersey

Warren Crown has designed
educational software for
classroom use, and has
worked as an educator
of mathematics teachers
at Rutgers for the past
30 years.

Francis (Skip) Fennell
L. Stanley Bowlsbey Professor of
    Education and Graduate and
    Professional Studies
McDaniel College
Westminster, Maryland

Skip Fennell is a mathematics
educator and has experience
as a classroom teacher, a
principal, and a supervisor of
instruction. He is currently the
L. Stanley Bowlsbey Professor
of Education and Graduate
and Professional Studies at
McDaniel College (note to
reader: this is an endowed
chair) and a past President
of the National Council of
Teachers of Mathematics.

Skip was a member of
the writing teams for the
Principles and Standards for
School Mathematics (NCTM,
2000), Curriculum Focal
Points (NCTM, 2006), and
the Common Core State
Standards (CCSSO, 2010).
He also served as a member
of the National Mathematics
Advisory Panel from May
2006 to April 2008.

Jane F. Schielack
Professor of Mathematics
Associate Dean for Assessment and
    Pre K–12 Education, College
    of Science
Texas A&M University
College Station, Texas

Janie Schielack works with
preservice and inservice
teachers to improve their
understanding of the
mathematical knowledge
needed for teaching. She was
the Chair of the writing team
for the NCTM Curriculum
Focal Points.

Janie was a member of the
Common Core State Standards
NCTM Review/Input Group.

William F. Tate IV
Edward Mallinckrodt
Distinguished University
    Professor in Arts & Sciences
Washington University
St. Louis, Missouri

Bill Tate is known for his
research focused on the social
determinates of mathematics
education attainment and
disparities. He is the recipient
of a presidential citation from
the American Educational
Research Association
for his conceptual and
methodological contributions
to the opportunity to learn
literature.

Focus and Coherence

by Randall I. Charles

> *...what and how students are taught should reflect not only the topics that fall within a certain academic discipline, but also the key ideas that determine how knowledge is organized and generated within that discipline.*

Common Core State Standards Initiative 2010, p. 3

The **Common Core State Standards** (CCSS), released in June 2010, represent the work of numerous mathematicians and mathematics educators concerned about the state of K–12 mathematics education in the United States. A primary goal of the developers of the CCSS was to respond to the criticism of mathematics curricula in the United States being a mile wide and an inch deep by providing a roadmap to "more ***focused and coherent*** [curricula] in order to improve mathematics achievement in this country" (Common Core State Standards Initiative, 2010, p. 3). *enVisionMATH Common Core* fully embraces the focus and coherence called for in the CCSS, and expands upon them in a significant way.

A focused and coherent mathematics curriculum provides in-depth instruction on a limited number of important categories of mathematics content. The CCSS identifies and organizes these important categories of mathematics content standards, to which *enVisionMATH Common Core* is directly aligned, and calls them critical areas. The grade-specific critical areas further organize related content into domains, and each domain organizes related content standards into clusters (see pages 8 and 9). Every lesson and topic in *enVisionMATH Common Core* correlates to the critical areas, domains, and content clusters.

enVisionMATH Common Core is unique in that it extends focus and coherence beyond just providing in-depth instruction on a limited number of important categories of mathematics content. The program extends focus and coherence by making explicit the Big Ideas in mathematics that students need to know and by showing how those ideas are related. A Big Idea in mathematics (called a Key Idea in the CCSS) is a statement of an *idea* that is central to learning mathematics; it links numerous smaller ideas (called **Essential Understandings** in *enVisionMATH Common Core*) into a coherent whole (Charles 2005). *enVisionMATH Common Core* connects all CCSS content standards to **Big Ideas** and **Essential Understandings**.

Big Ideas in *enVisionMATH Common Core* run across critical areas and grades; they connect ideas across content topics, and this is one reason they are "big." To illustrate this, the Big Idea called *Equivalence* is outlined on the next page, showing how it correlates to the content standards and to Essential Understandings across grades.

To convey the power of Big Ideas to students, they are translated into student-friendly **Essential Questions** presented at the beginning of each topic. Essential Questions focus students' attention on what they will be learning throughout a topic and what they will be able to do and understand at the end of a topic.

Big Idea: Equivalence

Any number, measure, numerical expression, algebraic expression, or equation can be represented in an infinite number of ways that have the same value.

Content Standards	Related Essential Understandings
K.OA.3 Decompose numbers less than or equal to 10 into pairs. . . .	• There is more than one way to show a number.
1.OA.6 Add and subtract within 20. . . .	• The number 10 can be broken into parts of the whole in different ways.
2.MD.8 Solve word problems involving dollar bills, quarters, dimes, nickels, and pennies. . . .	• The same amount of money can often be represented using different combinations of coins and bills.
3.NBT.2 Fluently add and subtract within 1000. . . .	• An equation shows a balance between what is on the right side and what is on the left side of the equal sign.
4.NBT.5 Multiply a whole number . . . by a one-digit whole number. . . .	• Different numerical expressions can have the same value. Or, the value of one expression can be less than (or greater than) the value of the other expression.
5.NBT.7 Add, subtract, multiply, and divide decimals to hundredths. . . .	• A number divided by a decimal can be represented as an equivalent calculation using place value to change the divisor to a whole number.
6.RP.3 Use ratio and rate reasoning to solve real-world and mathematical problems. . . .	• A part of a whole or a part of a set can be represented by a fraction, a decimal, and a percent.

Conclusion: Why do focus and coherence matter?

A focused and coherent mathematics curriculum makes possible in-depth student understanding, which in turn leads to higher student achievement. Knowing that the myriad of content topics in the high school mathematics curriculum coalesce into six conceptual categories helps students understand mathematics—they see the "whole," not just the "parts." And, when students know that mathematics is grounded on Big Ideas, not just skills, and that those ideas are connected, they better understand mathematics. *enVisionMATH Common Core* embraces and enhances the focus and coherence vision of the CCSS, leading to higher achievement for all.

> " *enVisionMATH Common Core organizes content using exactly the same structure as the Standards for Mathematical Content. Topics are organized by Domain, and all Topics for each Domain are grouped together. The focus and coherence provided by this structure allow enVisionMATH Common Core to cultivate both the procedures and the understanding called for in the Common Core State Standards.* "

References

Charles, Randall I. "Big Ideas and Understandings as the Foundation for Elementary and Middle School Mathematics." Journal of Mathematics Education Leadership, 8 no.1 (2005): 9–24.
Common Core State Standards Initiative. Common Core State Standards for Mathematics. Washington, D.C., 2010.

Common Core Standards and enVisionMATH

Critical Areas	Domains	Clusters
	5.OA Operations and Algebraic Thinking	**Write and interpret numerical expressions.** Standards: 5.OA.1, 5.OA.2 **Analyze patterns and relationships.** Standard: 5.OA.3
Extending division to 2-digit divisors, integrating decimal fractions into the place value system and developing understanding of operations with decimals to hundredths, and developing fluency with whole number and decimal operations	**5.NBT** Number and Operations in Base Ten	**Understand the place value system.** Standards: 5.NBT.1, 5.NBT.2, 5.NBT.3, 5.NBT.4 **Perform operations with multi-digit whole numbers and with decimals to hundredths.** Standards: 5.NBT.5, 5.NBT.6, 5.NBT.7
Developing fluency with addition and subtraction of fractions, and developing understanding of the multiplication of fractions and of division of fractions in limited cases (unit fractions divided by whole numbers and whole numbers divided by unit fractions)	**5.NF** Number and Operations— Fractions	**Use equivalent fractions as a strategy to add and subtract fractions.** Standards: 5.NF.1, 5.NF.2 **Apply and extend previous understandings of multiplication and division to multiply and divide fractions.** Standards: 5.NF.3, 5.NF.4, 5.NF.5, 5.NF.6, 5.NF.7
Developing understanding of volume	**5.MD** Measurement and Data	**Convert like measurement units within a given measurement system.** Standard: 5.MD.1 **Represent and interpret data.** Standard: 5.MD.2 **Geometric measurement: understand concepts of volume and relate volume to multiplication and to addition.** Standards: 5.MD.3, 5.MD.4, 5.MD.5
	5.G Geometry	**Graph points on the coordinate plane to solve real-world and mathematical problems.** Standards: 5.G.1, 5.G.2 **Classify two-dimensional figures into categories based on their properties.** Standards: 5.G.3, 5.G.4

The alignment of Critical Areas with Domains and Clusters is not straightforward in some cases. This chart shows one interpretation for Grade 5.

Grade 5 Topics	Grade 5 Big Ideas
Topic 8 Numerical Expressions, Patterns, and Relationships	• Equivalence • Properties • Patterns, Relations, and Functions • Variable • Solving Equations and Inequalities • Practices, Processes, and Proficiencies
Topic 1 Place Value **Topic 2** Adding and Subtracting Decimals **Topic 3** Multiplying Whole Numbers **Topic 4** Dividing by 1-Digit Divisors **Topic 5** Dividing by 2-Digit Divisors **Topic 6** Multiplying Decimals **Topic 7** Dividing Decimals	• Number Uses, Classification, and Representation • Numbers and the Number Line • The Base-Ten Numeration System • Equivalence • Comparison and Relationships • Properties • Basic Facts and Algorithms • Estimation • Patterns, Relations, and Functions • Practices, Processes, and Proficiencies
Topic 9 Adding and Subtracting Fractions **Topic 10** Adding and Subtracting Mixed Numbers **Topic 11** Multiplying and Dividing Fractions and Mixed Numbers	• Number Uses, Classification, and Representation • Numbers and the Number Line • Equivalence • Operation Meanings and Relationships • Basic Facts and Algorithms • Estimation • Practices, Processes, and Proficiencies
Topic 12 Volume of Solids **Topic 13** Units of Measure **Topic 14** Data	• Geometric Figures • Measurement • Data Collection and Representation • Practices, Processes, and Proficiencies
Topic 15 Classifying Plane Figures **Topic 16** Coordinate Geometry	• Patterns, Relations, and Functions • Geometric Figures • Practices, Processes, and Proficiencies

Big Ideas

Big Ideas	Grade K Topics	Grade 1 Topics	Grade 2 Topics	Grade 3 Topics	Grade 4 Topics	Grade 5 Topics	Grade 6 Topics
1 **Number Uses, Classification, and Representation** Numbers can be used for different purposes, and numbers can be classified and represented in different ways.	1, 2, 3, 5, 6, 11	3, 7, 8	5, 10	1	11	1, 3, 9	1, 5, 7
2 **Numbers and the Number Line** The set of real numbers is infinite and ordered. Whole numbers, integers, and fractions are real numbers. Each real number can be associated with a unique point on the number line.	4	16	8, 9	1, 9, 10	12, 13	2, 9, 10	5, 6,10
3 **The Base-Ten Numeration System** The base-ten numeration system is a scheme for recording numbers using digits 0–9, groups of ten, and place value.	6, 10	7, 8, 9	5, 10	1	3, 13	1, 7	1
4 **Equivalence** Any number, measure, numerical expression, algebraic expression, or equation can be represented in an infinite number of ways that have the same value.	9	3, 8	12, 13	2, 8, 10	4, 6, 11, 12, 13	4, 7, 8, 9, 10, 11	1, 3, 5, 6, 14, 16
5 **Comparison and Relationships** Numbers, expressions, measures, and objects can be compared and related to other numbers, expressions, measures, and objects in different ways.	2, 4, 12, 15	4, 9, 12	2, 3, 5, 10, 15	1, 10	3, 11, 13	1, 7	1, 12
6 **Operation Meanings and Relationships** There are multiple interpretations of addition, subtraction, multiplication, and division of rational numbers, and each operation is related to other operations.	7, 8, 9	1, 2, 3, 4, 6	1, 3, 4, 9, 15	2, 4, 6, 7, 8	1, 9, 10, 12	10, 11	8, 9
7 **Estimation** Numbers can be approximated by numbers that are close. Numerical calculations can be approximated by replacing numbers with other numbers that are close and easy to compute with mentally. Some measurements can be approximated using known referents as the unit in the measurement process.			14	2, 9	3, 4, 5, 7, 9, 10, 14	2, 3, 4, 5, 6, 7, 9, 10, 11	3, 7, 8, 9, 14, 15
8 **Properties** For a given set of numbers there are relationships that are always true, called properties, and these are the rules that govern arithmetic and algebra.		1, 5	2, 8	2, 3, 4, 6, 8	1	3, 8	2, 4
9 **Basic Facts and Algorithms** There is more than one algorithm for each of the operations with rational numbers. Some strategies for basic facts and most algorithms for operations with rational numbers, both mental math and paper and pencil, use equivalence to transform calculations into simpler ones.		4, 5, 10, 11	2, 3, 6, 7, 8, 9, 10, 11, 14	2, 3, 6	1, 4, 5, 6, 7, 8, 10, 12	2, 3, 4, 5, 6, 7, 9, 10	2, 3, 7, 8, 9, 16
10 **Variable** Mathematical situations and structures can be translated and represented abstractly using variables, expressions, and equations.				8	1	8	2

Big Ideas

	Big Ideas	Grade K Topics	Grade 1 Topics	Grade 2 Topics	Grade 3 Topics	Grade 4 Topics	Grade 5 Topics	Grade 6 Topics
11	**Solving Equations and Inequalities** Rules of arithmetic and algebra can be used together with notions of equivalence to transform equations and inequalities so solutions can be found.						8	1, 3, 4, 7, 9, 15
12	**Ratio and Proportionality** When mathematical or real-world quantities have a relationship that can be stated as "for every x units of the first quantity there are y units of the second quantity," this relationship can be described using a ratio. Proportionality involves a relationship in which the ratio of two quantities remains constant as the corresponding values of the quantities change. In a proportional relationship there are an infinite number of ratios equal to the lowest terms or constant ratio.							12, 13, 14, 15
13	**Patterns, Relations, and Functions** Relationships can be described and generalizations made for mathematical situations that have numbers or objects that repeat in predictable ways. For some relationships, mathematical expressions and equations can be used to describe how members of one set are related to members of a second set.	6	1, 7	5, 6, 7, 10	5	1, 2, 5, 7, 9, 14	2, 3, 4, 5, 6, 8, 16	1, 2, 5, 15
14	**Geometric Figures** Two- and three-dimensional objects with or without curved surfaces can be described, classified, and analyzed by their attributes. An object's location in space can be described quantitatively.	13, 14, 16	15	12	11	16	12, 15, 16	10,11, 18
15	**Measurement** Some attributes of objects are measurable and can be quantified using unit amounts.		12, 13	13, 15, 16	12, 13 14, 15	14, 15, 16	13	16, 17, 18
16	**Data Collection and Representation** Some questions can be answered by collecting and analyzing data, and the question to be answered determines the data that need to be collected and how best to collect the data. Data can be represented visually using tables, charts, and graphs. The type of data determines the best choice of visual representation.	13	14	16	16	15	14	19
17	**Data Distribution** There are special numerical measures that describe the center and spread of numerical data sets. The most appropriate measures for a situation depend on the nature of the data and on the use to be made of the measures.							19
18	**Practices, Processes, and Proficiencies** Mathematics content and practices can be applied to solve problems.	1–16	1–16	1–16	1–16	1–16	1–16	1–19

Critical Content Areas

(1) Developing fluency with addition and subtraction of fractions, and developing understanding of the multiplication of fractions and of division of fractions in limited cases (unit fractions divided by whole numbers and whole numbers divided by unit fractions);

(2) Extending division to 2-digit divisors, integrating decimal fractions into the place value system and developing understanding of operations with decimals to hundredths, and developing fluency with whole number and decimal operations;

(3) Developing understanding of volume.

Grade 5 students draw from their knowledge of operations with whole numbers and of fractions to add and subtract fractions and mixed numbers with unlike denominators. They apply their understandings of these concepts to explore both the meaning of and procedures for multiplying fractions and mixed numbers. From their work multiplying fractions, students can explain why the product of a whole number and a fraction greater than 1 is greater than the whole number while the product of a whole number and a fraction less than 1 is less than the whole number. Students explore the division of unit fractions by whole numbers and whole numbers by unit fractions, drawing once again on their knowledge of operations and fractions.

Grade 5 students finalize fluency with multi-digit operations (addition, subtraction, multiplication, and division), using the standard algorithm. They extend their knowledge of the place-value system to understand and work with decimals to thousandths. They apply their knowledge of operations to add, subtract, multiply, and divide decimals to hundredths.

Students in Grade 5 extend their study of geometric attributes to three-dimensional shapes. They explore volume and come to understand that the unit cube is the standard unit for measuring volume. They develop and apply formulas for finding the volume of rectangular prisms.

New Approaches

The **Common Core State Standards** promote the development of not just conceptual and procedural understandings of operations, but also an analytic framework from which students can begin to see patterns in the way operations function. With the multiplication of fractions, students are encouraged to understand the operations conceptually as the result of a sequence of operations or as a number of parts of a partition divided into equal parts—for example, $\frac{2}{3} \times 5$ can be thought of as $(2 \times 5) \div 3$. Students use visual models to show the multiplication of fractions and story contexts to give the operations meaning. Students also see multiplication as scaling, or resizing. Such an approach builds deeper conceptual understanding of the process of multiplication and builds on earlier work with fractions in which the fraction $\frac{a}{b}$ is interpreted as a multiple of the unit fraction.

Students use visual models to show the multiplication of fractions and story contexts to give the operations meaning.

Students begin their study of division of fractions by interpreting fractions as the division of the numerator by the denominator, and they express the quotient of whole-number division as a fraction (e.g., 4 apples shared equally by 6 people means each person gets $\frac{4}{6}$ of an apple). As they did with the multiplication of fractions, students explore division of fractions by dividing a unit fraction by a whole number and vice versa (a whole number divided by a unit fraction). Students are once again encouraged to use visual models to show the division of a fraction by a whole number and to create story contexts to give the operation meaning. Students continue to use the relationship between multiplication and division to explain and verify solutions to division problems. Such an approach builds deeper conceptual understanding of the operation of division.

> *Students' study of volume begins with an exploration of the unit cube as the unit of measure.*

Students' study of volume begins with an exploration of the unit cube as the unit of measure. Students interact with volume conceptually, recognizing that volume represents packing a solid with equal-sized units, and then explore processes to find the formula mathematically. Students apply the volume formula for right rectangular prisms.

What's Different?

Unlike many state curriculum frameworks, the **Common Core State Standards** do not present a spiral curriculum in which students revisit numerous topics from one year to the next with progressively more complex study. Rather, the CCSS identify a limited number of topics at each grade level, allowing enough time for students to achieve mastery of these concepts. The subsequent year of study builds on the concepts of the previous year. While some review of topics from earlier grades is appropriate and encouraged, the CCSS writers argue that reteaching of these topics should not be needed.

Certain topics that have often been part of the Grade 5 curriculum are not included in the CCSS. Among the most noticeable are a pared-down set of geometry and data-analysis standards, and the absence of probability concepts. Other topics, such as operations with fractions and decimals, have been shifted to different grades.

- **Number and Operations** The study of percents and ratios begins in Grade 6.

- **Measurement** The study of temperature is not part of the CCSS. The study of circles begins in Grade 7. The study of angles and angle measurement takes place in Grade 4.

- **Geometry** The CCSS introduce the study of congruence and transformations in Grade 8. While students in Kindergarten through Grade 2 explore three-dimensional shapes, compose them and compare and contrast them to two-dimensional shapes, students do not revisit three-dimensional shapes until Grade 5 with the study of volume.

- **Data Analysis** Students represent data in picture or bar graphs in Grades 2 and 3, but have limited experiences with other data displays except line plots. The study of measures of center begins in Grade 6.

- **Probability** Students first encounter probability concepts in Grade 7.

Common Core

Standards for Mathematical Practice

✔ Make sense of problems and persevere in solving them.

✔ Reason abstractly and quantitatively.

✔ Construct viable arguments and critique the reasoning of others.

✔ Model with mathematics.

✔ Use appropriate tools strategically.

✔ Attend to precision.

✔ Look for and make use of structure.

✔ Look for and express regularity in repeated reasoning.

Grade 5 Domain Colors

● **Domain: Operations and Algebraic Thinking**
Topic: 8

● **Domain: Number and Operations in Base Ten**
Topics: 1, 2, 3, 4, 5, 6, and 7

● **Domain: Number and Operations—Fractions**
Topics: 9, 10, and 11

● **Domain: Measurement and Data**
Topics: 12, 13, and 14

● **Domain: Geometry**
Topics: 15 and 16

Pacing Guide A Program Paced for Success

The pacing supports 1 lesson per day. There are 120 grade-level lessons and 10 Step-Up lessons to prepare for next year. Additional time may be spent on review, remediation, differentiation, formative and summative assessment as needed.

6 days	Topic 1	Place Value
8 days	Topic 2	Adding and Subtracting Decimals
9 days	Topic 3	Multiplying Whole Numbers
7 days	Topic 4	Dividing by 1-Digit Divisors
8 days	Topic 5	Dividing by 2-Digit Divisors
7 days	Topic 6	Multiplying Decimals
7 days	Topic 7	Dividing Decimals
9 days	Topic 8	Numerical Expressions, Patterns, and Relationships
10 days	Topic 9	Adding and Subtracting Fractions
7 days	Topic 10	Adding and Subtracting Mixed Numbers
11 days	Topic 11	Multiplying and Dividing Fractions and Mixed Numbers
7 days	Topic 12	Volume of Solids
7 days	Topic 13	Units of Measure
5 days	Topic 14	Data
6 days	Topic 15	Classifying Plane Figures
6 days	Topic 16	Coordinate Geometry
10 days	Step-Up	Step-Up to Grade 6 Lessons
130 days		

Standards for Mathematical Content

Critical Area Extending division to 2-digit divisors, integrating decimal fractions into the place value system and developing understanding of operations with decimals to hundredths, and developing fluency with whole number and decimal operations.

Domain Number and Operations in Base Ten

Cluster Understand the place value system.

Standards 5.NBT.1, 5.NBT.3, 5.NBT.3.a, 5.NBT.3.b

Topic 1 Place Value

Standards for Mathematical Content

Critical Area Extending division to 2-digit divisors, integrating decimal fractions into the place value system and developing understanding of operations with decimals to hundredths, and developing fluency with whole number and decimal operations.

Domain Number and Operations in Base Ten

Cluster Understand the place value system.

Cluster Perform operations with multi-digit whole numbers and with decimals to hundredths.

Standards 5.NBT.4, 5.NBT.7

Topic 2 Adding and Subtracting Decimals

Grade 5 enVisionMATH Contents

Standards for Mathematical Content

Critical Area Extending division to 2-digit divisors, integrating decimal fractions into the place value system and developing understanding of operations with decimals to hundredths, and developing fluency with whole number and decimal operations.

Domain Number and Operations in Base Ten

Cluster Understand the place value system.

Cluster Perform operations with multi-digit whole numbers and with decimals to hundredths.

Standards 5.NBT.2, 5.NBT.5, 5.NBT.6, 5.OA.1, 5.OA.2

Topic 3 Multiplying Whole Numbers

Standards for Mathematical Content

Critical Area Extending division to 2-digit divisors, integrating decimal fractions into the place value system and developing understanding of operations with decimals to hundredths, and developing fluency with whole number and decimal operations.

Domain Number and Operations in Base Ten

Cluster Perform operations with multi-digit whole numbers and with decimals to hundredths.

Standard 5.NBT.6

Topic 4 Dividing by 1-Digit Divisors

Standards for Mathematical Content

Critical Area Extending division to 2-digit divisors, integrating decimal fractions into the place value system and developing understanding of operations with decimals to hundredths, and developing fluency with whole number and decimal operations.

Domain Number and Operations in Base Ten

Cluster Perform operations with multi-digit whole numbers and with decimals to hundredths.

Standard 5.NBT.6

Topic 5 Dividing by 2-Digit Divisors

Standards for Mathematical Content

Critical Area Extending division to 2-digit divisors, integrating decimal fractions into the place value system and developing understanding of operations with decimals to hundredths, and developing fluency with whole number and decimal operations.

Domain Number and Operations in Base Ten

Cluster Understand the place value system.

Cluster Perform operations with multi-digit whole numbers and with decimals to hundredths.

Standards 5.NBT.1, 5.NBT.2, 5.NBT.7

Topic 6 Multiplying Decimals

Grade 5 enVisionMATH Contents

Standards for Mathematical Content

Critical Area Extending division to 2-digit divisors, integrating decimal fractions into the place value system and developing understanding of operations with decimals to hundredths, and developing fluency with whole number and decimal operations.

Domain Number and Operations in Base Ten

Cluster Understand the place value system.

Cluster Perform operations with multi-digit whole numbers and with decimals to hundredths.

Standards 5.NBT.1, 5.NBT.2, 5.NBT.7

Topic 7 Dividing Decimals

Standards for Mathematical Content

Connections to Critical Areas

Domain Operations and Algebraic Thinking

Cluster Write and interpret numerical expressions.

Cluster Analyze patterns and relationships.

Standards 5.OA.1, 5.OA.2, 5.OA.3

Topic 8 Numerical Expressions, Patterns, and Relationships

Standards for Mathematical Content

Critical Area Developing fluency with addition and subtraction of fractions, and developing understanding of the multiplication of fractions and of division of fractions in limited cases (unit fractions divided by whole numbers and whole numbers divided by unit fractions).

Domain Number and Operations—Fractions

Cluster Use equivalent fractions as a strategy to add and subtract fractions.

Standards 5.NF.1, 5.NF.2

Topic 9 Adding and Subtracting Fractions

Standards for Mathematical Content

Critical Area Developing fluency with addition and subtraction of fractions, and developing understanding of the multiplication of fractions and of division of fractions in limited cases (unit fractions divided by whole numbers and whole numbers divided by unit fractions).

Domain Number and Operations—Fractions

Cluster Use equivalent fractions as a strategy to add and subtract fractions.

Standards 5.NF.1, 5.NF.2

Topic 10 Adding and Subtracting Mixed Numbers

Grade 5 enVisionMATH Contents

Standards for Mathematical Content

Critical Area Developing fluency with addition and subtraction of fractions, and developing understanding of the multiplication of fractions and of division of fractions in limited cases (unit fractions divided by whole numbers and whole numbers divided by unit fractions).

Domain Number and Operations—Fractions

Cluster Apply and extend previous understandings of multiplication and division to multiply and divide fractions.

Standards 5.NF.3, 5.NF.4, 5.NF.4.a, 5.NF.4.b, 5.NF.5, 5.NF.5.a, 5.NF.5.b, 5.NF.6, 5.NF.7, 5.NF.7.a, 5.NF.7.b, 5.NF.7.c

Topic 11 Multiplying and Dividing Fractions and Mixed Numbers

Standards for Mathematical Content

Critical Area Developing understanding of volume.

Domain Measurement and Data

Cluster Geometric meaurement: understand concepts of volume and relate volume to multiplication and to addition.

Standards 5.MD.3, 5.MD.3.a, 5.MD.3.b, 5.MD.4, 5.MD.5, 5.MD.5.a, 5.MD.5.b, 5.MD.5.c

Topic 12 Volume of Solids

Standards for Mathematical Content

Critical Area Developing understanding of volume.

Domain Measurement and Data

Cluster Convert like measurement units within a given measurement system.

Standard 5.MD.1

Topic 13 Units of Measure

Standards for Mathematical Content

Connections to Critical Areas

Domain Measurement and Data

Cluster Represent and interpret data.

Standards 5.MD.2, 5.G.2

Topic 14 Data

Topic 15 Classifying Plane Figures

Standards for Mathematical Content

Connections to Critical Areas

Domain Geometry

Cluster Classify two-dimensional figures into categories based on their properties.

Standards 5.G.3, 5.G.4

Topic 16 Coordinate Geometry

Standards for Mathematical Content

Connections to Critical Areas

Domain Geometry

Cluster Graph points on the coordinate plane to solve real-world and mathematical problems.

Standards 5.G.1, 5.G.2, 5.OA.3

1 Make sense of problems and persevere in solving them.

Mathematically proficient students start by explaining to themselves the meaning of a problem and looking for entry points to its solution. They analyze givens, constraints, relationships, and goals. They make conjectures about the form and meaning of the solution and plan a solution pathway rather than simply jumping into a solution attempt. They consider analogous problems, and try special cases and simpler forms of the original problem in order to gain insight into its solution. They monitor and evaluate their progress and change course if necessary. Older students might, depending on the context of the problem, transform algebraic expressions or change the viewing window on their graphing calculator to get the information they need. Mathematically proficient students can explain correspondences between equations, verbal descriptions, tables, and graphs or draw diagrams of important features and relationships, graph data, and search for regularity or trends. Younger students might rely on using concrete objects or pictures to help conceptualize and solve a problem. Mathematically proficient students check their answers to problems using a different method, and they continually ask themselves, "Does this make sense?" They can understand the approaches of others to solving complex problems and identify correspondences between different approaches.

enVisionMATH Common Core is built on a foundation of problem-based instruction that has sense-making at its heart. The Problem Solving Handbook, found on pages xiii–xxiii, presents to students a process that begins with making sense of the problem. *Read and Understand,* the first phase of the process, has students ask themselves, *What am I trying to find?* and *What do I know?,* questions that will help identify the givens and constraints of the problem. In the second phase, *Plan and Solve,* students decide on a solution plan. The Problem-Solving Recording Sheet, a reproducible teaching resource, provides a structured outline to help students make sense of the problem and implement a workable solution method. In the final phase, *Look Back and Check,* students verify that their work is reasonable and reflects the information given.

Each lesson begins with **Problem-Based Interactive Learning,** an activity in which students interact with their peers and teachers to make sense of and decide on a workable solution for a real-world situation. Another feature of each lesson is the set of problem-solving exercises in which students persevere by applying different skills and strategies to solve problems. Each topic includes at least one problem-solving lesson in which students focus on honing their sense-making and problem-solving skills.

Found throughout the program; some examples:

Lesson 1-3	Lesson 5-4	Lesson 9-2	Lesson 13-1
Lesson 2-3	Lesson 6-5	Lesson 10-4	Lesson 14-4
Lesson 3-3	Lesson 7-7	Lesson 11-8	Lesson 15-4
Lesson 4-6	Lesson 8-7	Lesson 12-6	Lesson 16-6

2 Reason abstractly and quantitatively.

Mathematically proficient students make sense of quantities and their relationships in problem situations. They bring two complementary abilities to bear on problems involving quantitative relationships: the ability to *decontextualize*—to abstract a given situation and represent it symbolically and manipulate the representing symbols as if they have a life of their own, without necessarily attending to their referents—and the ability to *contextualize,* to pause as needed during the manipulation process in order to probe into the referents for the symbols involved. Quantitative reasoning entails habits of creating a coherent representation of the problem at hand; considering the units involved; attending to the meaning of quantities, not just how to compute them; and knowing and flexibly using different properties of operations and objects.

enVisionMATH Common Core provides scaffolded instruction to help students develop both quantitative and abstract reasoning. In the **Visual Learning Bridge**, students can see how to represent a given situation numerically or algebraically. They will have opportunities later in the lesson to reason abstractly as they endeavor to represent situations symbolically. Reasonableness exercises remind students to compare their work to the original situation. In the **Do You Understand?** part of the Guided Practice, students gain experiences with quantitative reasoning as they consider the meaning of different parts of an expression or equation. Reasoning problems throughout the exercise sets focus students' attention on the structure or meaning of an operation, for example, rather than merely the solution.

Found throughout the program; some examples:

Lesson 1-5	Lesson 5-5	Lesson 9-10	Lesson 13-1
Lesson 2-6	Lesson 6-4	Lesson 10-1	Lesson 14-1
Lesson 3-4	Lesson 7-4	Lesson 11-7	Lesson 15-1
Lesson 4-1	Lesson 8-7	Lesson 12-7	Lesson 16-5

3 Construct viable arguments and critique the reasoning of others.

Mathematically proficient students understand and use stated assumptions, definitions, and previously established results in constructing arguments. They make conjectures and build a logical progression of statements to explore the truth of their conjectures. They are able to analyze situations by breaking them into cases, and can recognize and use counterexamples. They justify their conclusions, communicate them to others, and respond to the arguments of others. They reason inductively about data, making plausible arguments that take into account the context from which the data arose. Mathematically proficient students are also able to compare the effectiveness of two plausible arguments, distinguish correct logic or reasoning from that which is flawed, and—if there is a flaw in an argument—explain what it is. Elementary students can construct arguments using concrete referents such as objects, drawings, diagrams, and actions. Such arguments can make sense and be correct, even though they are not generalized or made formal until later grades. Later, students learn to determine domains to which an argument applies. Students at all grades can listen or read the arguments of others, decide whether they make sense, and ask useful questions to clarify or improve the arguments.

Consistent with a focus on reasoning and sense-making is a focus on critical reasoning — argumentation and critique of arguments. In Pearson's *enVisionMATH Common Core*, the **Problem-Based Interactive Learning** affords students opportunities to share with classmates their thinking about problems, their solution methods, and their reasoning about the solutions. The many Reasoning exercises found throughout the program specifically call for students to justify or explain their solutions. **Writing to Explain** exercises help students develop foundational critical reasoning skills by having them construct explanations for processes. The ability to articulate a clear explanation for a process is a stepping stone to critical analysis and reasoning of both the student's own processes and those of others.

Found throughout the program; some examples:

Lesson 1-1	**Lesson 5-6**	**Lesson 9-6**	**Lesson 13-5**
Lesson 2-6	**Lesson 6-6**	**Lesson 10-4**	**Lesson 14-3**
Lesson 3-9	**Lesson 7-2**	**Lesson 11-2**	**Lesson 15-2**
Lesson 4-3	**Lesson 8-4**	**Lesson 12-5**	**Lesson 16-2**

4 Model with mathematics.

Mathematically proficient students can apply the mathematics they know to solve problems arising in everyday life, society, and the workplace. In early grades, this might be as simple as writing an addition equation to describe a situation. In middle grades, a student might apply proportional reasoning to plan a school event or analyze a problem in the community. By high school, a student might use geometry to solve a design problem or use a function to describe how one quantity of interest depends on another. Mathematically proficient students who can apply what they know are comfortable making assumptions and approximations to simplify a complicated situation, realizing that these may need revision later. They are able to identify important quantities in a practical situation and map their relationships using such tools as diagrams, two-way tables, graphs, flowcharts and formulas. They can analyze those relationships mathematically to draw conclusions. They routinely interpret their mathematical results in the context of the situation and reflect on whether the results make sense, possibly improving the model if it has not served its purpose.

Students in Pearson's *enVisionMATH Common Core* are introduced to mathematical modeling in the early grades. They first use manipulatives and drawings and then equations to model addition and subtraction situations. The **Visual Learning Bridge** and **Visual Learning Animation** often present real-world situations, and students are shown how these can be modeled mathematically. In later grades, students expand their modeling skills to include representations such as tables and graphs, as well as equations.

Found throughout the program; some examples:

Lesson 1-4	**Lesson 5-5**	**Lesson 9-10**	**Lesson 13-2**
Lesson 2-1	**Lesson 6-4**	**Lesson 10-7**	**Lesson 14-5**
Lesson 3-6	**Lesson 7-1**	**Lesson 11-1**	**Lesson 15-6**
Lesson 4-5	**Lesson 8-5**	**Lesson 12-2**	**Lesson 16-3**

5 Use appropriate tools strategically.

Mathematically proficient students consider the available tools when solving a mathematical problem. These tools might include pencil and paper, concrete models, a ruler, a protractor, a calculator, a spreadsheet, a computer algebra system, a statistical package, or dynamic geometry software. Proficient students are sufficiently familiar with tools appropriate for their grade or course to make sound decisions about when each of these tools might be helpful, recognizing both the insight to be gained and their limitations. For example, mathematically proficient high school students analyze graphs of functions and solutions generated using a graphing calculator. They detect possible errors by strategically using estimation and other mathematical knowledge. When making mathematical models, they know that technology can enable them to visualize the results of varying assumptions, explore consequences, and compare predictions with data. Mathematically proficient students at various grade levels are able to identify relevant external mathematical resources, such as digital content located on a website, and use them to pose or solve problems. They are able to use technological tools to explore and deepen their understanding of concepts.

Students become fluent in the use of a wide assortment of tools ranging from physical objects, including manipulatives, rulers, protractors, and even pencil and paper, to digital tools, such as eTools, calculators, and computers. As students become more familiar with the tools available to them, they are able to begin making decisions about which tools are most helpful in a particular situation.

Throughout the program; some examples:

Lesson 1-2	**Lesson 5-3**	**Lesson 10-2**	**Lesson 13-4**
Lesson 2-4	**Lesson 6-4**	**Lesson 11-7**	**Lesson 14-3**
Lesson 3-8	**Lesson 8-2**	**Lesson 12-6**	**Lesson 15-5**
Lesson 4-7	**Lesson 9-5**	**Lesson 12-7**	**Lesson 16-6**

6 Attend to precision.

Mathematically proficient students try to communicate precisely to others. They try to use clear definitions in discussion with others and in their own reasoning. They state the meaning of the symbols they choose, including using the equal sign consistently and appropriately. They are careful about specifying units of measure, and labeling axes to clarify the correspondence with quantities in a problem. They calculate accurately and efficiently, express numerical answers with a degree of precision appropriate for the problem context. In the elementary grades, students give carefully formulated explanations to each other. By the time they reach high school they have learned to examine claims and make explicit use of definitions.

Students are expected to use mathematical terms and symbols with precision. Key terms and concepts are highlighted in each lesson. In the **Do You Understand?** feature, students revisit these key terms or concepts and provide explicit definitions or explanations. For the **Writing to Explain** and **Think About the Structure** exercises, students are asked to use precise language to provide clear explanations of terms, concepts, or processes. Students are reminded to use appropriate units of measure in their solutions as well as in labels for diagrams, graphs, and other kinds of displays.

Throughout the program; some examples:

Lesson 1-6	**Lesson 5-1**	**Lesson 9-3**	**Lesson 13-3**
Lesson 2-5	**Lesson 6-6**	**Lesson 10-6**	**Lesson 14-1**
Lesson 3-6	**Lesson 7-4**	**Lesson 11-6**	**Lesson 15-4**
Lesson 4-4	**Lesson 8-3**	**Lesson 12-7**	**Lesson 16-1**

7 Look for and make use of structure.

Mathematically proficient students look closely to discern a pattern or structure. Young students, for example, might notice that three and seven more is the same amount as seven and three more, or they may sort a collection of shapes according to how many sides the shapes have. Later, students will see 7×8 equals the well-remembered $7 \times 5 + 7 \times 3$, in preparation for learning about the distributive property. In the expression $x^2 + 9x + 14$, older students can see the 14 as 2×7 and the 9 as $2 + 7$. They recognize the significance of an existing line in a geometric figure and can use the strategy of drawing an auxiliary line for solving problems. They also can step back for an overview and shift perspective. They can see complicated things, such as some algebraic expressions, as single objects or as being composed of several objects. For example, they can see $5 - 3(x + y)^2$ as 5 minus a positive number times a square and use that to realize that its value cannot be more than 5 for any real numbers x and y.

Students are encouraged to look for structure as they develop solution plans. In the **Look for a Pattern** problem-solving lessons, children in the early years develop a sense of patterning with visual and physical objects. As students mature in their mathematical thinking, they look for structure in numerical operations by focusing on place value and properties of operations. This focus on looking for and recognizing structure enables students to draw from patterns as they formalize their thinking about the structure of operations.

Throughout the program; some examples:

Lesson 1-3	Lesson 5-2	Lesson 10-3	Lesson 15-1
Lesson 2-7	Lesson 6-1	Lesson 11-4	Lesson 16-4
Lesson 3-1	Lesson 7-5	Lesson 12-4	
Lesson 3-5	Lesson 8-9	Lesson 13-7	
Lesson 4-2	Lesson 9-5	Lesson 14-4	

8 Look for and express regularity in repeated reasoning.

Mathematically proficient students notice if calculations are repeated, and look both for general methods and for shortcuts. Upper elementary students might notice when dividing 25 by 11 that they are repeating the same calculations over and over again, and conclude they have a repeating decimal. By paying attention to the calculation of slope as they repeatedly check whether points are on the line through (1, 2) with slope 3, middle school students might abstract the equation $(y - 2)/(x - 1) = 3$. Noticing the regularity in the way terms cancel when expanding $(x - 1)(x + 1)$, $(x - 1)(x^2 + x + 1)$, and $(x - 1)(x^3 + x^2 + x + 1)$ might lead them to the general formula for the sum of a geometric series. As they work to solve a problem, mathematically proficient students maintain oversight of the process, while attending to the details. They continually evaluate the reasonableness of their intermediate results.

Students are prompted to look for repetition in computations to help them develop shortcuts and become more efficient problem-solvers. Students are reminded to think about problems they have encountered previously that may share features or processes. They are encouraged to draw on the solution plan developed for such problems, and as their mathematical thinking matures, to look for and apply generalizations to similar situations. The **Problem-Based Interactive Learning** activities offer students opportunities to look for regularity in the way operations behave.

Throughout the program; some examples:

Lesson 1-6	Lesson 6-2	Lesson 10-2	Lesson 15-6
Lesson 2-2	Lesson 7-3	Lesson 11-5	Lesson 16-4
Lesson 3-5	Lesson 8-2	Lesson 12-3	
Lesson 4-6	Lesson 9-4	Lesson 13-6	
Lesson 5-7	Lesson 9-9	Lesson 14-2	

Grade 5 Standards for Mathematical Content Correlation

DOMAIN 5.OA Operations and Algebraic Thinking

Write and interpret numerical expressions.

Common Core State Standard	Student's Edition Pages	Teacher's Edition Pages*
5.OA.1 Use parentheses, brackets, or braces in numerical expressions, and evaluate expressions with these symbols.	**72–73,** Lesson 3-5 **85,** Reteaching Set E **196–199,** Lesson 8-2 **200–201,** Lesson 8-3 **202–203,** Lesson 8-4 **214,** Reteaching Set B	**72A–73B,** Lesson 3-5 **85,** Reteaching Set E **196A–199B,** Lesson 8-2 **200A–201B,** Lesson 8-3 **202A–203B,** Lesson 8-4 **214,** Reteaching Set B
5.OA.2 Write simple expressions that record calculations with numbers, and interpret numerical expressions without evaluating them. *For example, express the calculation "add 8 and 7, then multiply by 2" as $2 \times (8 + 7)$. Recognize that $3 \times (18932 + 921)$ is three times as large as $18932 + 921$ without having to calculate the indicated sum or product.*	**82–83,** Lesson 3-9 **85,** Reteaching Set G **110–111,** Lesson 4-7 **112,** Reteaching Set C **194–195,** Lesson 8-1 **210–211,** Lesson 8-8 **212–213,** Lesson 8-9 **214–215,** Reteaching Sets A, D, E	**82A–83B,** Lesson 3-9 **85,** Reteaching Set G **110A–111B,** Lesson 4-7 **112,** Reteaching Set C **194A–195B,** Lesson 8-1 **210A–211B,** Lesson 8-8 **212A–213B,** Lesson 8-9 **214–215,** Reteaching Sets A, D, E

Analyze patterns and relationships.

5.OA.3 Generate two numerical patterns using two given rules. Identify apparent relationships between corresponding terms. Form ordered pairs consisting of corresponding terms from the two patterns, and graph the ordered pairs on a coordinate plane. *For example, given the rule "Add 3" and the starting number 0, and given the rule "Add 6" and the starting number 0, generate terms in the resulting sequences, and observe that the terms in one sequence are twice the corresponding terms in the other sequence. Explain informally why this is so.*	**204–205,** Lesson 8-5 **206–207,** Lesson 8-6 **208–209,** Lesson 8-7 **215,** Reteaching Set C **402–403,** Lesson 16-5 **407,** Reteaching Set D	**204A–205B,** Lesson 8-5 **206A–207B,** Lesson 8-6 **208A–209B,** Lesson 8-7 **215,** Reteaching Set C **402A–403B,** Lesson 16-5 **407,** Reteaching Set D

***Teacher's Resource Masters** for every lesson (Practice, Reteaching, Enrichment, Centers, Quick Check) are considered part of this correlation.

Understand the place value system.

Common Core State Standard	Student's Edition Pages	Teacher's Edition Pages*
5.NBT.1 Recognize that in a multi-digit number, a digit in one place represents 10 times as much as it represents in the place to its right and 1/10 of what it represents in the place to its left.	**6–7,** Lesson 1-1 **8–11,** Lesson 1-2 **12–13,** Lesson 1-3 **22,** Reteaching Sets A–C **146–147,** Lesson 6-1 **162,** Reteaching Set A **170–171,** Lesson 7-1 **186,** Reteaching Set A	**6A–7B,** Lesson 1-1 **8A–11B,** Lesson 1-2 **12A–13B,** Lesson 1-3 **22,** Reteaching Sets A–C **146A–147B,** Lesson 6-1 **162,** Reteaching Set A **170A–171B,** Lesson 7-1 **186,** Reteaching Set A
5.NBT.2 Explain patterns in the number of zeros of the product when multiplying a number by powers of 10, and explain patterns in the placement of the decimal point when a decimal is multiplied or divided by a power of 10. Use whole-number exponents to denote powers of 10.	**66–67,** Lesson 3-2 **70–71,** Lesson 3-4 **84,** Reteaching Sets B, D **146–147,** Lesson 6-1 **162,** Reteaching Set A **170–171,** Lesson 7-1 **186,** Reteaching Set A	**66A–67B,** Lesson 3-2 **70A–71B,** Lesson 3-4 **84,** Reteaching Sets B, D **146A–147B,** Lesson 6-1 **162,** Reteaching Set A **170A–171B,** Lesson 7-1 **186,** Reteaching Set A
5.NBT.3 Read, write, and compare decimals to thousandths.	**18–21,** Lesson 1-6 **23,** Reteaching Set F	**18A–21B,** Lesson 1-6 **23,** Reteaching Set F
5.NBT.3.a Read and write decimals to thousandths using base-ten numerals, number names, and expanded form, e.g., $347.392 = 3 \times 100 + 4 \times 10 + 7 \times 1 + 3 \times (1/10) + 9 \times (1/100) + 2 \times (1/1000)$.	**8–11,** Lesson 1-2 **12–13,** Lesson 1-3 **14–15,** Lesson 1-4 **22–23,** Reteaching Sets B–D	**8A–11B,** Lesson 1-2 **12A–13B,** Lesson 1-3 **14A–15B,** Lesson 1-4 **22–23,** Reteaching Sets B–D
5.NBT.3.b Compare two decimals to thousandths based on meanings of the digits in each place, using >, =, and < symbols to record the results of comparisons.	**16–17,** Lesson 1-5 **23,** Reteaching Set E	**16A–17B,** Lesson 1-5 **23,** Reteaching Set E
5.NBT.4 Use place value understanding to round decimals to any place.	**34–35,** Lesson 2-2 **54,** Reteaching Set B	**34A–35B,** Lesson 2-2 **54,** Reteaching Set B

*Teacher's Resource Masters for every lesson (Practice, Reteaching, Enrichment, Centers, Quick Check) are considered part of this correlation.

DOMAIN 5.NBT Number and Operations in Base Ten *cont.*

Perform operations with multi-digit whole numbers and with decimals to hundredths.

Common Core State Standard	Student's Edition Pages	Teacher's Edition Pages*
5.NBT.5 Fluently multiply multi-digit whole numbers using the standard algorithm.	**68–69,** Lesson 3-3 **72–73,** Lesson 3-5 **74–77,** Lesson 3-6 **78–79,** Lesson 3-7 **80–81,** Lesson 3-8 **82–83,** Lesson 3-9 **84–85,** Reteaching Sets C, E, F, G	**68A–69B,** Lesson 3-3 **72A–73B,** Lesson 3-5 **74A–77B,** Lesson 3-6 **78A–79B,** Lesson 3-7 **80A–81B,** Lesson 3-8 **82A–83B,** Lesson 3-9 **84–85,** Reteaching Sets C, E, F, G
5.NBT.6 Find whole-number quotients of whole numbers with up to four-digit dividends and two-digit divisors, using strategies based on place value, the properties of operations, and/or the relationship between multiplication and division. Illustrate and explain the calculation by using equations, rectangular arrays, and/or area models.	**64–65,** Lesson 3-1 **84,** Reteaching Set A **92–93,** Lesson 4-1 **94–95,** Lesson 4-2 **96–97,** Lesson 4-3 **98–101,** Lesson 4-4 **102–105,** Lesson 4-5 **106–109,** Lesson 4-6 **110–111,** Lesson 4-7 **112–113,** Reteaching Sets A–E **120–121,** Lesson 5-1 **122–123,** Lesson 5-2 **124–125,** Lesson 5-3 **126–127,** Lesson 5-4 **128–131,** Lesson 5-5 **132–133,** Lesson 5-6 **134–135,** Lesson 5-7 **136–137,** Lesson 5-8 **138–139,** Reteaching Sets A–F	**64A–65B,** Lesson 3-1 **84,** Reteaching Set A **92A–93B,** Lesson 4-1 **94A–95B,** Lesson 4-2 **96A–97B,** Lesson 4-3 **98A–101B,** Lesson 4-4 **102A–105B,** Lesson 4-5 **106A–109B,** Lesson 4-6 **110A–111B,** Lesson 4-7 **112–113,** Reteaching Sets A–E **120A–121B,** Lesson 5-1 **122A–123B,** Lesson 5-2 **124A–125B,** Lesson 5-3 **126A–127B,** Lesson 5-4 **128A–131B,** Lesson 5-5 **132A–133B,** Lesson 5-6 **134A–135B,** Lesson 5-7 **136A–137B,** Lesson 5-8 **138–139,** Reteaching Sets A–F
5.NBT.7 Add, subtract, multiply, and divide decimals to hundredths, using concrete models or drawings and strategies based on place value, properties of operations, and/or the relationship between addition and subtraction; relate the strategy to a written method and explain the reasoning used.	**30–33,** Lesson 2-1 **36–39,** Lesson 2-3 **40–43,** Lesson 2-4 **44–45,** Lesson 2-5 **46–47,** Lesson 2-6 **48–49,** Lesson 2-7 **50–53,** Lesson 2-8 **54–57,** Reteaching Sets A, C–H **146–147,** Lesson 6-1 **148–149,** Lesson 6-2 **150–151,** Lesson 6-3 **152–155,** Lesson 6-4 **156–157,** Lesson 6-5 **158–159,** Lesson 6-6 **160–161,** Lesson 6-7 **162–163,** Reteaching Sets A–D **170–171,** Lesson 7-1 **172–173,** Lesson 7-2 **174–175,** Lesson 7-3 **176–177,** Lesson 7-4 **178–179,** Lesson 7-5 **180–181,** Lesson 7-6 **182–185,** Lesson 7-7 **186–187,** Reteaching Sets A–E	**30A–33B,** Lesson 2-1 **36A–39B,** Lesson 2-3 **40A–43B,** Lesson 2-4 **44A–45B,** Lesson 2-5 **46A–47B,** Lesson 2-6 **48A–49B,** Lesson 2-7 **50A–53B,** Lesson 2-8 **54–57,** Reteaching Sets A, C–H **146A–147B,** Lesson 6-1 **148A–149B,** Lesson 6-2 **150A–151B,** Lesson 6-3 **152A–155B,** Lesson 6-4 **156A–157B,** Lesson 6-5 **158A–159B,** Lesson 6-6 **160A–161B,** Lesson 6-7 **162–163,** Reteaching Sets A–D **170A–171B,** Lesson 7-1 **172A–173B,** Lesson 7-2 **174A–175B,** Lesson 7-3 **176A–177B,** Lesson 7-4 **178A–179B,** Lesson 7-5 **180A–181B,** Lesson 7-6 **182A–185B,** Lesson 7-7 **186–187,** Reteaching Sets A–E

*Teacher's Resource Masters for every lesson (Practice, Reteaching, Enrichment, Centers, Quick Check) are considered part of this correlation.

Use equivalent fractions as a strategy to add and subtract fractions.

Common Core State Standard	Student's Edition Pages	Teacher's Edition Pages*
5.NF.1 Add and subtract fractions with unlike denominators (including mixed numbers) by replacing given fractions with equivalent fractions in such a way as to produce an equivalent sum or difference of fractions with like denominators. *For example, 2/3 + 5/4 = 8/12 + 15/12 = 23/12. (In general, a/b + c/d = (ad + bc)/bd.)*	**222–223,** Lesson 9-1 **224–225,** Lesson 9-2 **228–229,** Lesson 9-4 **230–231,** Lesson 9-5 **232–233,** Lesson 9-6 **234–235,** Lesson 9-7 **236–237,** Lesson 9-8 **238–239,** Lesson 9-9 **240–243,** Lesson 9-10 **244–245,** Reteaching Sets A, C–G **252–253,** Lesson 10-1 **254–255,** Lesson 10-2 **256–259,** Lesson 10-3 **260–261,** Lesson 10-4 **262–263,** Lesson 10-5 **264–265,** Lesson 10-6 **266–267,** Lesson 10-7 **268–269,** Reteaching Sets A–F	**222A–223B,** Lesson 9-1 **224A–225B,** Lesson 9-2 **228A–229B,** Lesson 9-4 **230A–231B,** Lesson 9-5 **232A–233B,** Lesson 9-6 **234A–235B,** Lesson 9-7 **236A–237B,** Lesson 9-8 **238A–239B,** Lesson 9-9 **240A–243B,** Lesson 9-10 **244–245,** Reteaching Sets A, C–G **252A–253B,** Lesson 10-1 **254A–255B,** Lesson 10-2 **256A–259B,** Lesson 10-3 **260A–261B,** Lesson 10-4 **262A–263B,** Lesson 10-5 **264A–265B,** Lesson 10-6 **266A–267B,** Lesson 10-7 **268–269,** Reteaching Sets A–F
5.NF.2 Solve word problems involving addition and subtraction of fractions referring to the same whole, including cases of unlike denominators, e.g., by using visual fraction models or equations to represent the problem. Use benchmark fractions and number sense of fractions to estimate mentally and assess the reasonableness of answers. *For example, recognize an incorrect result 2/5 + 1/2 = 3/7, by observing that 3/7 < 1/2.*	**224–225,** Lesson 9-2 **226–227,** Lesson 9-3 **228–229,** Lesson 9-4 **230–231,** Lesson 9-5 **232–233,** Lesson 9-6 **234–235,** Lesson 9-7 **236–237,** Lesson 9-8 **238–239,** Lesson 9-9 **240–243,** Lesson 9-10 **244–245,** Reteaching Sets A–G **252–253,** Lesson 10-1 **254–255,** Lesson 10-2 **256–259,** Lesson 10-3 **260–261,** Lesson 10-4 **262–263,** Lesson 10-5 **264–265,** Lesson 10-6 **266–267,** Lesson 10-7 **268–269,** Reteaching Sets A–F	**224A–225B,** Lesson 9-2 **226A–227B,** Lesson 9-3 **228A–229B,** Lesson 9-4 **230A–231B,** Lesson 9-5 **232A–233B,** Lesson 9-6 **234A–235B,** Lesson 9-7 **236A–237B,** Lesson 9-8 **238A–239B,** Lesson 9-9 **240A–243B,** Lesson 9-10 **244–245,** Reteaching Sets A–G **252A–253B,** Lesson 10-1 **254A–255B,** Lesson 10-2 **256A–259B,** Lesson 10-3 **260A–261B,** Lesson 10-4 **262A–263B,** Lesson 10-5 **264A–265B,** Lesson 10-6 **266A–267B,** Lesson 10-7 **268–269,** Reteaching Sets A–F

*Teacher's Resource Masters for every lesson (Practice, Reteaching, Enrichment, Centers, Quick Check) are considered part of this correlation.

DOMAIN 5.NF **Number and Operations—Fractions** *cont.*

Apply and extend previous understandings of multiplication and division to multiply and divide fractions.

Common Core State Standard	Student's Edition Pages	Teacher's Edition Pages*
5.NF.3 Interpret a fraction as division of the numerator by the denominator ($a/b = a \div b$). Solve word problems involving division of whole numbers leading to answers in the form of fractions or mixed numbers, e.g., by using visual fraction models or equations to represent the problem. *For example, interpret 3/4 as the result of dividing 3 by 4, noting that 3/4 multiplied by 4 equals 3, and that when 3 wholes are shared equally among 4 people each person has a share of size 3/4. If 9 people want to share a 50-pound sack of rice equally by weight, how many pounds of rice should each person get? Between what two whole numbers does your answer lie?*	**276–277,** Lesson 11-1 **300,** Reteaching Set A	**276A–277B,** Lesson 11-1 **300,** Reteaching Set A
5.NF.4 Apply and extend previous understandings of multiplication to multiply a fraction or whole number by a fraction.	**278–279,** Lesson 11-2 **282–285,** Lesson 11-4 **286–287,** Lesson 11-5 **288–289,** Lesson 11-6 **300,** Reteaching Sets B–D	**278A–279B,** Lesson 11-2 **282A–285B,** Lesson 11-4 **286A–287B,** Lesson 11-5 **288A–289B,** Lesson 11-6 **300,** Reteaching Sets B–D
5.NF.4.a Interpret the product $(a/b) \times q$ as a parts of a partition of q into b equal parts; equivalently, as the result of a sequence of operations $a \times q \div b$. *For example, use a visual fraction model to show $(2/3) \times 4 = 8/3$, and create a story context for this equation. Do the same with $(2/3) \times (4/5) = 8/15$. (In general, $(a/b) \times (c/d) = ac/bd$.)*	**278–279,** Lesson 11-2 **282–285,** Lesson 11-4 **288–289,** Lesson 11-6 **300,** Reteaching Sets B–D	**278A–279B,** Lesson 11-2 **282A–285B,** Lesson 11-4 **288A–289B,** Lesson 11-6 **300,** Reteaching Sets B–D
5.NF.4.b Find the area of a rectangle with fractional side lengths by tiling it with unit squares of the appropriate unit fraction side lengths, and show that the area is the same as would be found by multiplying the side lengths. Multiply fractional side lengths to find areas of rectangles, and represent fraction products as rectangular areas.	**286–287,** Lesson 11-5 **300,** Reteaching Set C	**286A–287B,** Lesson 11-5 **300,** Reteaching Set C

*Teacher's Resource Masters for every lesson (Practice, Reteaching, Enrichment, Centers, Quick Check) are considered part of this correlation.

Common Core State Standard	Student's Edition Pages	Teacher's Edition Pages*
5.NF.5 Interpret multiplication as scaling (resizing), by:	**290–291,** Lesson 11-7 **300,** Reteaching Set B	**290A–291B,** Lesson 11-7 **300,** Reteaching Set B
5.NF.5.a Comparing the size of a product to the size of one factor on the basis of the size of the other factor, without performing the indicated multiplication.	**280–281,** Lesson 11-3 **290–291,** Lesson 11-7 **300,** Reteaching Sets B, D	**280A–281B,** Lesson 11-3 **290A–291B,** Lesson 11-7 **300,** Reteaching Sets B, D
5.NF.5.b Explaining why multiplying a given number by a fraction greater than 1 results in a product greater than the given number (recognizing multiplication by whole numbers greater than 1 as a familiar case); explaining why multiplying a given number by a fraction less than 1 results in a product smaller than the given number; and relating the principle of fraction equivalence $a/b = (n \times a)/(n \times b)$ to the effect of multiplying a/b by 1.	**280–281,** Lesson 11-3 **290–291,** Lesson 11-7 **300,** Reteaching Sets B, D	**280A–281B,** Lesson 11-3 **290A–291B,** Lesson 11-7 **300,** Reteaching Sets B, D
5.NF.6 Solve real world problems involving multiplication of fractions and mixed numbers, e.g., by using visual fraction models or equations to represent the problem.	**292–293,** Lesson 11-8 **301,** Reteaching Set E	**292A–293B,** Lesson 11-8 **301,** Reteaching Set E

*Teacher's Resource Masters for every lesson (Practice, Reteaching, Enrichment, Centers, Quick Check) are considered part of this correlation.

DOMAIN 5.NF **Number and Operations—Fractions** *cont.*

Common Core State Standard	Student's Edition Pages	Teacher's Edition Pages*
5.NF.7 Apply and extend previous understandings of division to divide unit fractions by whole numbers and whole numbers by unit fractions.[1]	**294–295,** Lesson 11-9 **296–297,** Lesson 11-10 **298–299,** Lesson 11-11 **301,** Reteaching Sets F, G	**294A–295B,** Lesson 11-9 **296A–297B,** Lesson 11-10 **298A–299B,** Lesson 11-11 **301,** Reteaching Sets F, G
5.NF.7.a Interpret division of a unit fraction by a non-zero whole number, and compute such quotients. *For example, create a story context for (1/3) ÷ 4, and use a visual fraction model to show the quotient. Use the relationship between multiplication and division to explain that (1/3) ÷ 4 = 1/12 because (1/12) × 4 = 1/3.*	**298–299,** Lesson 11-11 **301,** Reteaching Set F	**298A–299B,** Lesson 11-11 **301,** Reteaching Set F
5.NF.7.b Interpret division of a whole number by a unit fraction, and compute such quotients. *For example, create a story context for 4 ÷ (1/5), and use a visual fraction model to show the quotient. Use the relationship between multiplication and division to explain that 4 ÷ (1/5) = 20 because 20 × (1/5) = 4.*	**294–295,** Lesson 11-9 **301,** Reteaching Set F	**294A–295B,** Lesson 11-9 **301,** Reteaching Set F
5.NF.7.c Solve real world problems involving division of unit fractions by non-zero whole numbers and division of whole numbers by unit fractions, e.g., by using visual fraction models and equations to represent the problem. *For example, how much chocolate will each person get if 3 people share 1/2 lb of chocolate equally? How many 1/3-cup servings are in 2 cups of raisins?*	**296–297,** Lesson 11-10 **301,** Reteaching Set G	**296A–297B,** Lesson 11-10 **301,** Reteaching Set G

*Teacher's Resource Masters for every lesson (Practice, Reteaching, Enrichment, Centers, Quick Check) are considered part of this correlation.

Convert like measurement units within a given measurement system.

Common Core State Standard	Student's Edition Pages	Teacher's Edition Pages*
5.MD.1 Convert among different-sized standard measurement units within a given measurement system (e.g., convert 5 cm to 0.05 m), and use these conversions in solving multi-step, real world problems.	**332–333,** Lesson 13-1 **334–335,** Lesson 13-2 **336–337,** Lesson 13-3 **338–339,** Lesson 13-4 **340–341,** Lesson 13-5 **342–343,** Lesson 13-6 **344–345,** Lesson 13-7 **346–347,** Reteaching Sets A–G	**332A–333B,** Lesson 13-1 **334A–335B,** Lesson 13-2 **336A–337B,** Lesson 13-3 **338A–339B,** Lesson 13-4 **340A–341B,** Lesson 13-5 **342A–343B,** Lesson 13-6 **344A–345B,** Lesson 13-7 **346–347,** Reteaching Sets A–G

Represent and interpret data.

Common Core State Standard	Student's Edition Pages	Teacher's Edition Pages*
5.MD.2 Make a line plot to display a data set of measurements in fractions of a unit (1/2, 1/4, 1/8). Use operations on fractions for this grade to solve problems involving information presented in line plots. *For example, given different measurements of liquid in identical beakers, find the amount of liquid each beaker would contain if the total amount in all the beakers were redistributed equally.*	**354–355,** Lesson 14-1 **356–357,** Lesson 14-2 **358–359,** Lesson 14-3 **360–361,** Lesson 14-4 **364,** Reteaching Sets A–C	**354A–355B,** Lesson 14-1 **356A–357B,** Lesson 14-2 **358A–359B,** Lesson 14-3 **360A–361B,** Lesson 14-4 **364,** Reteaching Sets A–C

Geometric measurement: understand concepts of volume and relate volume to multiplication and to addition.

Common Core State Standard	Student's Edition Pages	Teacher's Edition Pages*
5.MD.3 Recognize volume as an attribute of solid figures and understand concepts of volume measurement.	**308–309,** Lesson 12-1 **324,** Reteaching Set A	**308A–309B,** Lesson 12-1 **324,** Reteaching Set A
5.MD.3.a A cube with side length 1 unit, called a "unit cube," is said to have "one cubic unit" of volume, and can be used to measure volume.	**310–311,** Lesson 12-2 **314–315,** Lesson 12-4 **324–325,** Reteaching Sets B, C	**310A–311B,** Lesson 12-2 **314A–315B,** Lesson 12-4 **324–325,** Reteaching Sets B, C
5.MD.3.b A solid figure which can be packed without gaps or overlaps using *n* unit cubes is said to have a volume of *n* cubic units.	**310–311,** Lesson 12-2 **314–315,** Lesson 12-4 **324–325,** Reteaching Sets B, C	**310A–311B,** Lesson 12-2 **314A–315B,** Lesson 12-4 **324–325,** Reteaching Sets B, C
5.MD.4 Measure volumes by counting unit cubes, using cubic cm, cubic in, cubic ft, and improvised units.	**310–311,** Lesson 12-2 **314–315,** Lesson 12-4 **322–323,** Lesson 12-7 **324–325,** Reteaching Sets B, C	**310A–311B,** Lesson 12-2 **314A–315B,** Lesson 12-4 **322A–323B,** Lesson 12-7 **324–325,** Reteaching Sets B, C

*Teacher's Resource Masters for every lesson (Practice, Reteaching, Enrichment, Centers, Quick Check) are considered part of this correlation.

DOMAIN 5.MD **Measurement and Data** *cont.*

Common Core State Standard	Student's Edition Pages	Teacher's Edition Pages*
5.MD.5 Relate volume to the operations of multiplication and addition and solve real world and mathematical problems involving volume.	**312–313,** Lesson 12-3 **316–319,** Lesson 12-5 **324–325,** Reteaching Sets B, D	**312A–313B,** Lesson 12-3 **316A–319B,** Lesson 12-5 **324–325,** Reteaching Sets B, D
5.MD.5.a Find the volume of a right rectangular prism with whole-number side lengths by packing it with unit cubes, and show that the volume is the same as would be found by multiplying the edge lengths, equivalently by multiplying the height by the area of the base. Represent threefold whole-number products as volumes, e.g., to represent the associative property of multiplication.	**314–315,** Lesson 12-4 **316–319,** Lesson 12-5 **325,** Reteaching Sets C, D	**314A–315B,** Lesson 12-4 **316A–319B,** Lesson 12-5 **325,** Reteaching Sets C, D
5.MD.5.b Apply the formulas $V = l \times w \times h$ and $V = b \times h$ for rectangular prisms to find volumes of right rectangular prisms with whole-number edge lengths in the context of solving real world and mathematical problems.	**316–319,** Lesson 12-5 **320–321,** Lesson 12-6 **325,** Reteaching Sets D, E	**316A–319B,** Lesson 12-5 **320A–321B,** Lesson 12-6 **325,** Reteaching Sets D, E
5.MD.5.c Recognize volume as additive. Find volumes of solid figures composed of two non-overlapping right rectangular prisms by adding the volumes of the non-overlapping parts, applying this technique to solve real world problems.	**320–321,** Lesson 12-6 **325,** Reteaching Set E	**320A–321B,** Lesson 12-6 **325,** Reteaching Set E

*Teacher's Resource Masters for every lesson (Practice, Reteaching, Enrichment, Centers, Quick Check) are considered part of this correlation.

Graph points on the coordinate plane to solve real-world and mathematical problems.

Common Core State Standard	Student's Edition Pages	Teacher's Edition Pages*
5.G.1 Use a pair of perpendicular number lines, called axes, to define a coordinate system, with the intersection of the lines (the origin) arranged to coincide with the 0 on each line and a given point in the plane located by using an ordered pair of numbers, called its coordinates. Understand that the first number indicates how far to travel from the origin in the direction of one axis, and the second number indicates how far to travel in the direction of the second axis, with the convention that the names of the two axes and the coordinates correspond (e.g., x-axis and x-coordinate, y-axis and y-coordinate).	**392–395,** Lesson 16-1 **396–397,** Lesson 16-2 **398–399,** Lesson 16-3 **400–401,** Lesson 16-4 **404–405,** Lesson 16-6 **406–407,** Reteaching Sets A–E	**392A–395B,** Lesson 16-1 **396A–397B,** Lesson 16-2 **398A–399B,** Lesson 16-3 **400A–401B,** Lesson 16-4 **404A–405B,** Lesson 16-6 **406–407,** Reteaching Sets A–E
5.G.2 Represent real world and mathematical problems by graphing points in the first quadrant of the coordinate plane, and interpret coordinate values of points in the context of the situation.	**362–363,** Lesson 14-5 **365,** Reteaching Set D **400–401,** Lesson 16-4 **402–403,** Lesson 16-5 **404–405,** Lesson 16-6 **407,** Reteaching Sets D, E	**362A–363B,** Lesson 14-5 **365,** Reteaching Set D **400A–401B,** Lesson 16-4 **402A–403B,** Lesson 16-5 **404A–405B,** Lesson 16-6 **407,** Reteaching Sets D, E
Classify two-dimensional figures into categories based on their properties.		
5.G.3 Understand that attributes belonging to a category of two-dimensional figures also belong to all subcategories of that category. *For example, all rectangles have four right angles and squares are rectangles, so all squares have four right angles.*	**372–373,** Lesson 15-1 **374–375,** Lesson 15-2 **376–377,** Lesson 15-3 **378–379,** Lesson 15-4 **382–383,** Lesson 15-6 **384–385,** Reteaching Sets A–D, F	**372A–373B,** Lesson 15-1 **374A–375B,** Lesson 15-2 **376A–377B,** Lesson 15-3 **378A–379B,** Lesson 15-4 **382A–383B,** Lesson 15-6 **384–385,** Reteaching Sets A–D, F
5.G.4 Classify two-dimensional figures in a hierarchy based on properties.	**376–377,** Lesson 15-3 **378–379,** Lesson 15-4 **380–381,** Lesson 15-5 **382–383,** Lesson 15-6 **384–385,** Reteaching Sets C–F	**376A–377B,** Lesson 15-3 **378A–379B,** Lesson 15-4 **380A–381B,** Lesson 15-5 **382A–383B,** Lesson 15-6 **384–385,** Reteaching Sets C–F

*Teacher's Resource Masters for every lesson (Practice, Reteaching, Enrichment, Centers, Quick Check) are considered part of this correlation.

Notes

1. Students able to multiply fractions in general can develop strategies to divide fractions in general, by reasoning about the relationship between multiplication and division. But division of a fraction by a fraction is not a requirement at this grade.

Common Core

Standards for Mathematical Practice

Throughout the program, students at every grade level

- ✔ Make sense of problems and persevere in solving them.
- ✔ Reason abstractly and quantitatively.
- ✔ Construct viable arguments and critique the reasoning of others.
- ✔ Model with mathematics.
- ✔ Use appropriate tools strategically.
- ✔ Attend to precision.
- ✔ Look for and make use of structure.
- ✔ Look for and express regularity in repeated reasoning.

Common Core Domains

Domain **Counting and Cardinality**

	K	1	2	3	4	5	6
Know number names and the count sequence.							
Count to 100 by ones.	**K.CC.1** Topic 6						
Count to 100 by tens.	**K.CC.1** Topic 6						
Count forward from a given number.	**K.CC.2** Topics 4–6						
Write numbers from 0 to 20.	**K.CC.3** Topics 1–3, 5						
Represent up to 20 objects with a written numeral.	**K.CC.3** Topics 1–3, 5						
Count to tell the number of objects.							
Understand the relationship between numbers and quantities.	**K.CC.4** Topics 1–3						
Connect counting to cardinality.	**K.CC.4** Topics 1–3						
Count objects, saying the number names in the standard order.	**K.CC.4.a** Topics 1, 3						
Pair each object counted with one and only one number name and vice versa.	**K.CC.4.a** Topics 1, 3						
Connect the last number name said to the number of objects counted.	**K.CC.4.b** Topics 1–3, 5, 6						
Understand that the number of objects is the same regardless of how they were counted.	**K.CC.4.b** Topics 1, 5						
Understand that each successive number name represents one more.	**K.CC.4.c** Topics 2–4, 6						
Count up to 10 things in a scattered configuration.	**K.CC.5** Topics 1, 6						
Count up to 20 things in a line, rectangular array, or circle.	**K.CC.5** Topics 1, 6						
Count out up to 20 objects.	**K.CC.5** Topics 1–3, 6						
Compare numbers.							
Compare the number of objects in two groups.	**K.CC.6** Topics 2, 4						
Compare two numbers between 1 and 10.	**K.CC.7** Topic 4						

Domain **Operations and Algebraic Thinking**

	K	1	2	3	4	5	6
Understand addition as putting together and adding to, and understand subtraction as taking apart and taking from.							
Represent addition using a variety of models.	**K.OA.1** Topics 4, 7						
Represent subtraction using a variety of models.	**K.OA.1** Topics 4, 8						
Add within 10 using objects and drawings.	**K.OA.2** Topic 7						
Solve addition word problems within 10.	**K.OA.2** Topic 7						
Subtract within 10 using objects and drawings.	**K.OA.2** Topic 8						
Solve subtraction word problems within 10.	**K.OA.2** Topic 8						
Decompose numbers less than or equal to 10.	**K.OA.3** Topic 9						
Record decomposition of numbers less than or equal to 10.	**K.OA.3** Topic 9						
Make 10 using objects and drawings.	**K.OA.4** Topic 9						
Record how to make 10 using a drawing or equation.	**K.OA.4** Topic 9						
Fluently add within 5.	**K.OA.5** Topic 7						
Fluently subtract within 5.	**K.OA.5** Topic 8						
Represent and solve problems involving addition and subtraction.							
Add within 20 to solve word problems.		**1.OA.1** Topics 1, 4, 5					
Subtract within 20 to solve word problems.		**1.OA.1** Topics 2, 4, 6					
Solve word problems within 20 with three addends.		**1.OA.2** Topic 5					
Add within 100 to solve one-step word problems.			**2.OA.1** Topics 1–9				
Add within 100 to solve two-step word problems.			**2.OA.1** Topics 3, 9				
Subtract within 100 to solve one-step word problems.			**2.OA.1** Topics 1–9				
Subtract within 100 to solve two-step word problems.			**2.OA.1** Topics 3, 9				
Understand and apply properties of operations and the relationship between addition and subtraction.							
Apply properties of operations as strategies to add.		**1.OA.3** Topics 1, 4, 5					
Apply properties of operations as strategies to subtract.		**1.OA.3** Topics 2, 4, 6					
Understand subtraction as an unknown-addend problem.		**1.OA.4** Topics 2–4, 6					
Add and subtract within 20.							
Relate counting to addition.		**1.OA.5** Topics 3, 4					
Relate counting to subtraction.		**1.OA.5** Topics 3, 4					
Add within 20.		**1.OA.6** Topics 1, 4, 5					
Subtract within 20.		**1.OA.6** Topics 2, 4, 6					

Domain **Operations and Algebraic Thinking** *cont.*

	K	1	2	3	4	5	6
Use the relationship between addition and subtraction.		**1.OA.6** Topics 2, 4, 6					
Fluently add within 20 using mental strategies.			**2.OA.2** Topic 2				
Fluently subtract within 20 using mental strategies.			**2.OA.2** Topic 3				
Work with addition and subtraction equations.							
Understand the meaning of the equal sign.		**1.OA.7** Topics 1, 2					
Determine if equations involving addition are true or false.		**1.OA.7** Topics 4, 5					
Determine if equations involving subtraction are true or false.		**1.OA.7** Topics 2, 6					
Determine the unknown whole number in an addition equation.		**1.OA.8** Topics 1, 4–6					
Determine the unknown whole number in a subtraction equation.		**1.OA.8** Topics 2, 4, 6					
Work with equal groups of objects to gain foundations for multiplication.							
Work with even and odd numbers.			**2.OA.3** Topic 5				
Express an even number as a sum of two equal addends.			**2.OA.3** Topic 5				
Use addition to find the total number of objects in rectangular arrays.			**2.OA.4** Topic 4				
Represent and solve problems involving multiplication and division.							
Interpret products of whole numbers.				**3.OA.1** Topic 4			
Interpret whole-number quotients of whole numbers.				**3.OA.2** Topic 7			
Use multiplication within 100 to solve word problems.				**3.OA.3** Topics 4–6			
Use division within 100 to solve word problems.				**3.OA.3** Topics 7, 8			
Determine the unknown whole number in a multiplication equation.				**3.OA.4** Topics 7, 8			
Determine the unknown whole number in a division equation.				**3.OA.4** Topics 7, 8			
Understand properties of multiplication and the relationship between multiplication and division.							
Apply properties of multiplication.				**3.OA.5** Topics 4, 6			
Apply properties of division.				**3.OA.5** Topic 8			
Understand division as an unknown-factor problem.				**3.OA.6** Topic 7			
Multiply and divide within 100.							
Fluently multiply within 100.				**3.OA.7** Topic 5			
Fluently divide within 100.				**3.OA.7** Topic 8			
Solve problems involving the four operations, and identify and explain patterns in arithmetic.							
Solve two-step word problems.				**3.OA.8** Topics 2, 3, 5, 6, 8			
Assess the reasonableness of answers to two-step word problems.				**3.OA.8** Topics 2, 3, 5, 6, 8			

Scope and Sequence

Domain **Operations and Algebraic Thinking** *cont.*

	K	1	2	3	4	5	6
Identify and explain arithmetic patterns.				**3.OA.9** Topics 2, 4, 5, 7			
Use the four operations with whole numbers to solve problems.							
Relate multiplication equations to multiplicative comparison.					**4.OA.1** Topic 1		
Distinguish multiplicative comparison from additive comparison.					**4.OA.2** Topics 1, 9		
Multiply to solve word problems involving multiplicative comparison.					**4.OA.2** Topics 1, 9		
Divide to solve word problems involving multiplicative comparison.					**4.OA.2** Topics 1, 9		
Solve multi-step word problems.					**4.OA.3** Topics 1, 4–10		
Assess the reasonableness of answers to multi-step word problems.					**4.OA.3** Topics 1, 4–10		
Use algebraic equations to represent multi-step word problems.					**4.OA.3** Topics 1, 4–10		
Write and interpret numerical expressions.							
Use parentheses, brackets, or braces in numerical expressions.						**5.OA.1** Topics 3, 8	
Evaluate numerical expressions with parentheses, brackets, or braces.						**5.OA.1** Topics 3, 8	
Write numerical expressions that record calculations.						**5.OA.2** Topics 3, 4, 8	
Interpret numerical expressions.						**5.OA.2** Topics 3, 4, 8	
Gain familiarity with factors and multiples.							
Find factor pairs.					**4.OA.4** Topics 1, 11		
Recognize that a whole number is a multiple of each of its factors.					**4.OA.4** Topics 1, 11		
Determine whether one number is a multiple of another.					**4.OA.4** Topics 1, 11		
Identify prime or composite numbers.					**4.OA.4** Topic 11		
Generate and analyze patterns.							
Generate a number pattern that follows a given rule.					**4.OA.5** Topics 1, 2, 11, 16		
Generate a shape pattern that follows a given rule.					**4.OA.5** Topic 2		
Describe features of a pattern.					**4.OA.5** Topic 2		
Analyze patterns and relationships.							
Generate two numerical patterns using two given rules.						**5.OA.3** Topics 8, 16	
Identify relationships between corresponding terms in two numerical patterns.						**5.OA.3** Topics 8, 16	
Form ordered pairs from two numerical patterns.						**5.OA.3** Topic 16	
Graph ordered pairs generated by two patterns.						**5.OA.3** Topic 16	

Domain **Expressions and Equations**

	K	1	2	3	4	5	6
Apply and extend previous understandings of arithmetic to algebraic expressions.							
Write numerical expressions with exponents.							**6.EE.1** Topic 1
Evaluate numerical expressions with exponents.							**6.EE.1** Topic 1
Read and write algebraic expressions.							**6.EE.2** Topic 2
Evaluate algebraic expressions.							**6.EE.2** Topic 2
Write algebraic expressions that record operations.							**6.EE.2.a** Topic 2
Identify parts of an expression using mathematical terms.							**6.EE.2.b** Topic 2
View one or more parts of an expression as a single entity.							**6.EE.2.b** Topic 2
Evaluate expressions at specific values of their variables.							**6.EE.2.c** Topics 2, 3, 17
Evaluate expressions that arise from formulas.							**6.EE.2.c** Topic 17
Evaluate expressions using Order of Operations.							**6.EE.2.c** Topics 2, 3, 17
Generate equivalent expressions.							**6.EE.3** Topics 2, 4
Identify when two expressions are equivalent.							**6.EE.4** Topic 4
Reason about and solve one-variable equations and inequalities.							
Determine the values from a specified set that make an equation true.							**6.EE.5** Topics 3, 4
Determine the values from a specified set that make an inequality true.							**6.EE.5** Topics 3, 15
Solve problems by using variables to represent numbers and write expressions.							**6.EE.6** Topics 2–4
Understand how variables are used.							**6.EE.6** Topics 2–4
Write and solve equations of the form $x + p = q$.							**6.EE.7** Topics 4, 9, 15, 17
Write and solve equations of the form $px = q$.							**6.EE.7** Topics 4, 9, 15, 17
Write an inequality of the form $x > c$ or $x < c$.							**6.EE.8** Topic 15
Recognize that inequalities of the form $x > c$ or $x < c$ have infinitely many solutions.							**6.EE.8** Topic 15
Represent solutions of inequalities on number lines.							**6.EE.8** Topic 15
Represent and analyze quantitative relationships between dependent and independent variables.							
Use variables to represent two quantities that change in relationship to one another.							**6.EE.9** Topics 11, 12, 15
Analyze relationships between dependent and independent variables.							**6.EE.9** Topics 11, 12, 15

Domain **Number and Operations in Base Ten**

	K	1	2	3	4	5	6
Work with numbers 11–19 to gain foundations for place value.							
Compose and decompose numbers from 11 to 19 into ten ones and some further ones.	K.NBT.1 Topics 10, 11						
Record composition or decomposition.	K.NBT.1 Topics 10, 11						
Understand that numbers from 11 to 19 are composed of ten ones and one to nine ones.	K.NBT.1 Topics 10, 11						
Extend the counting sequence.							
Count to 120 from a given number.		1.NBT.1 Topic 7					
Read and write numerals to 120.		1.NBT.1 Topic 7					
Represent up to 120 objects with a written numeral.		1.NBT.1 Topic 7					
Understand place value.							
Understand that the two digits of a two-digit number represent amounts of tens and ones.		1.NBT.2 Topics 7–9					
Understand that 10 can be thought of as a bundle of ten ones — called a "ten."		1.NBT.2.a Topics 7, 8					
Understand that numbers from 11 to 19 are composed of ten ones and one to nine ones.		1.NBT.2.b Topic 7					
Understand that the numbers 10, 20, … 90 refer to one to nine tens (and 0 ones).		1.NBT.2.c Topics 7, 8					
Compare two two-digit numbers and use the symbols >, =, and <.		1.NBT.3 Topic 9					
Understand that the digits of a three-digit number represent amounts of hundreds, tens, and ones.			2.NBT.1 Topic 10				
Understand that 100 can be thought of as a bundle of ten tens — called a "hundred."			2.NBT.1.a Topic 10				
Understand that the numbers 100, 200, … 900 refer to one to nine hundreds (and 0 tens and 0 ones).			2.NBT.1.b Topic 5				
Count within 1000.			2.NBT.2 Topics 5, 6, 10				
Skip-count by 5s, 10s, and 100s.			2.NBT.2 Topic 10				
Read and write base-ten numerals to 1000.			2.NBT.3 Topics 5, 10				
Read and write number names to 1000.			2.NBT.3 Topics 5, 10				
Use expanded form for numbers to 1000.			2.NBT.3 Topic 10				
Compare two three-digit numbers and use the symbols >, =, and <.			2.NBT.4 Topics 5, 10				
Generalize place value understanding for multi-digit whole numbers.							
Recognize that a digit in one place represents ten times what it represents in the place to its right.					4.NBT.1 Topics 3, 10		
Read and write base-ten numerals for multi-digit numbers.					4.NBT.2 Topic 3		
Read and write number names for multi-digit numbers.					4.NBT.2 Topic 3		
Use expanded form for multi-digit numbers.					4.NBT.2 Topic 3		
Compare two multi-digit numbers and use the symbols >, =, and <.					4.NBT.2 Topic 3		

Domain **Number and Operations in Base Ten** *cont.*

	K	1	2	3	4	5	6
Round multi-digit whole numbers to any place.					**4.NBT.3** Topics 3–7		
Understand the place value system.							
Understand how the value of a digit in one place compares to the value in the place to its right or left.						**5.NBT.1** Topics 1, 6, 7	
Explain patterns of zeros when multiplying a number by powers of 10.						**5.NBT.2** Topics 3, 6	
Use exponents to denote powers of 10.						**5.NBT.2** Topics 3, 6, 7	
Explain patterns in the placement of the decimal point when a decimal is multiplied by a power of 10.						**5.NBT.2** Topic 6	
Explain patterns in the placement of the decimal point when a decimal is divided by a power of 10.						**5.NBT.2** Topic 7	
Read and write decimals to thousandths.						**5.NBT.3** Topic 1	
Compare decimals to thousandths.						**5.NBT.3** Topic 1	
Read and write decimals to thousandths using base-ten numerals and number names.						**5.NBT.3.a** Topic 1	
Use expanded form for decimals.						**5.NBT.3.a** Topic 1	
Compare decimals to thousandths using the symbols >, =, and <.						**5.NBT.3.b** Topic 1	
Round decimals to any place.						**5.NBT.4** Topic 2	
Use place value understanding and properties of operations to add and subtract.							
Add a two-digit number and a one-digit number.		**1.NBT.4** Topics 9, 10					
Add a two-digit number and a multiple of 10.		**1.NBT.4** Topics 9, 10					
Understand place-value concepts involved in adding two-digit numbers.		**1.NBT.4** Topics 9, 10					
Mentally find 10 more than a given number.		**1.NBT.5** Topics 9, 10					
Mentally find 10 less than a given number.		**1.NBT.5** Topics 9, 11					
Subtract multiples of 10.		**1.NBT.6** Topic 11					
Fluently add within 100.			**2.NBT.5** Topics 1–3, 5–9				
Fluently subtract within 100.			**2.NBT.5** Topics 1–3, 5–9				
Add up to four two-digit numbers.			**2.NBT.6** Topics 5, 8, 9				
Understand written methods for adding within 1000.			**2.NBT.7** Topics 7, 11				
Understand place-value concepts for addition within 1000.			**2.NBT.7** Topics 7, 11				
Subtract within 1000.			**2.NBT.7** Topics 7, 11				
Understand place-value concepts for subtraction within 1000.			**2.NBT.7** Topics 7, 11				
Mentally add 10 or 100.			**2.NBT.8** Topics 6, 10, 11				

Domain **Number and Operations in Base Ten** *cont.*

	K	1	2	3	4	5	6
Mentally subtract 10 or 100.			**2.NBT.8** Topics 7, 10, 11				
Explain why addition strategies work.			**2.NBT.9** Topics 2, 5, 8, 11, 14				
Explain why subtraction strategies work.			**2.NBT.9** Topics 3, 5, 7, 9, 11, 14				
Use place value understanding and properties of operations to perform multi-digit arithmetic.							
Round whole numbers to the nearest 10.				**3.NBT.1** Topics 1–3			
Round whole numbers to the nearest 100.				**3.NBT.1** Topics 1–3			
Fluently add within 1000.				**3.NBT.2** Topics 1–3			
Fluently subtract within 1000.				**3.NBT.2** Topics 1–3			
Fluently subtract within 1000 using the relationship between addition and subtraction.				**3.NBT.2** Topics 1–3			
Multiply one-digit whole numbers by multiples of 10.				**3.NBT.3** Topic 5			
Fluently add multi-digit whole numbers using the standard algorithm.					**4.NBT.4** Topic 4		
Fluently subtract multi-digit whole numbers using the standard algorithm.					**4.NBT.4** Topic 4		
Multiply up to a four-digit number by a one-digit number.					**4.NBT.5** Topics 5–10		
Multiply two two-digit numbers.					**4.NBT.5** Topics 7–10		
Model multi-digit multiplication.					**4.NBT.5** Topics 5–10		
Divide up to four-digit dividends by one-digit divisors.					**4.NBT.6** Topics 9, 10		
Model division of up to four-digit dividends by one-digit divisors.					**4.NBT.6** Topics 9, 10		
Perform operations with multi-digit whole numbers and with decimals to hundredths.							
Fluently multiply multi-digit whole numbers using the standard algorithm.						**5.NBT.5** Topic 3	
Divide up to four-digit dividends by two-digit divisors.						**5.NBT.6** Topic 5	
Model division of up to four-digit dividends by two-digit divisors.						**5.NBT.6** Topics 4, 5	
Add decimals to hundredths.						**5.NBT.7** Topic 2	
Subtract decimals to hundredths.						**5.NBT.7** Topic 2	
Subtract decimals using the relationship between addition and subtraction.						**5.NBT.7** Topic 2	
Multiply decimals to hundredths.						**5.NBT.7** Topic 6	
Divide decimals to hundredths.						**5.NBT.7** Topic 7	
Explain strategies used to perform decimal operations.						**5.NBT.7** Topics 2, 6, 7	

Domain Number and Operations—Fractions

	K	1	2	3	4	5	6
Develop understanding of fractions as numbers.							
Interpret proper fractions.				**3.NF.1** Topic 9			
Relate fractions to numbers on the number line.				**3.NF.2** Topics 9, 10			
Interpret and show unit fractions on the number line.				**3.NF.2.a** Topic 9			
Interpret and show fractions of the form a/b on the number line.				**3.NF.2.b** Topic 9			
Explain equivalence of fractions.				**3.NF.3** Topic 10			
Compare fractions by reasoning about their size.				**3.NF.3** Topic 10			
Relate fraction equivalence to size.				**3.NF.3.a** Topic 10			
Relate fraction equivalence to the number line.				**3.NF.3.a** Topic 10			
Generate and model equivalent fractions.				**3.NF.3.b** Topic 10			
Relate whole numbers and fractions.				**3.NF.3.c** Topic 10			
Compare two fractions with the same numerator or same denominator and use the symbols $>$, $=$, or $<$.				**3.NF.3.d** Topic 10			
Extend understanding of fraction equivalence and ordering.							
Explain why a fraction a/b is equivalent to a fraction $(n \times a)/(n \times b)$.					**4.NF.1** Topic 11		
Recognize and generate equivalent fractions.					**4.NF.1** Topic 11		
Compare two fractions with different numerators and different denominators and use the symbols $>$, $=$, or $<$.					**4.NF.2** Topic 11		
Build fractions from unit fractions by applying and extending previous understandings of operations on whole numbers.							
Understand a fraction a/b with $a > 1$ as a sum of fractions $1/b$.					**4.NF.3** Topic 12		
Interpret addition of fractions.					**4.NF.3.a** Topic 12		
Interpret subtraction of fractions.					**4.NF.3.a** Topic 12		
Decompose fractions.					**4.NF.3.b** Topic 12		
Add mixed numbers with like denominators.					**4.NF.3.c** Topic 12		
Subtract mixed numbers with like denominators.					**4.NF.3.c** Topic 12		
Solve word problems involving addition of fractions with like denominators.					**4.NF.3.d** Topic 12		
Solve word problems involving subtraction of fractions with like denominators.					**4.NF.3.d** Topic 12		
Multiply a fraction by a whole number.					**4.NF.4** Topic 13		
Understand a fraction a/b as a multiple of $1/b$.					**4.NF.4.a** Topic 13		
Understand that $n \times (a/b) = (n \times a)/b$.					**4.NF.4.b** Topic 13		
Solve word problems involving multiplication of a fraction by a whole number.					**4.NF.4.c** Topic 13		
Understand decimal notation for fractions, and compare decimal fractions.							
Express a fraction with denominator 10 as an equivalent fraction with denominator 100.					**4.NF.5** Topic 13		

Domain **Number and Operations—Fractions** *cont.*

	K	1	2	3	4	5	6
Use equivalent fractions to add two fractions with respective denominators 10 and 100.					**4.NF.5** Topic 13		
Use decimal notation for fractions with denominators 10 or 100.					**4.NF.6** Topic 13		
Use decimal notation to describe length.					**4.NF.6** Topic 13		
Show decimals on a number line.					**4.NF.6** Topic 13		
Compare two decimals to hundredths and use the symbols >, =, and <.					**4.NF.7** Topic 13		
Use equivalent fractions as a strategy to add and subtract fractions.							
Add fractions with unlike denominators.						**5.NF.1** Topic 9	
Add mixed numbers with unlike denominators.						**5.NF.1** Topic 10	
Subtract fractions with unlike denominators.						**5.NF.1** Topic 9	
Subtract mixed numbers with unlike denominators.						**5.NF.1** Topic 10	
Solve word problems involving addition of fractions.						**5.NF.2** Topics 9, 10	
Solve word problems involving subtraction of fractions.						**5.NF.2** Topics 9, 10	
Estimate mentally and assess the reasonableness of a fraction sum or difference.						**5.NF.2** Topics 9, 10	
Apply and extend previous understandings of multiplication and division to multiply and divide fractions.							
Interpret a fraction as division.						**5.NF.3** Topic 11	
Solve word problems involving division of whole numbers with answers that are fractions or mixed numbers.						**5.NF.3** Topic 11	
Multiply a whole number by a fraction.						**5.NF.4** Topic 11	
Multiply a fraction by a fraction.						**5.NF.4** Topic 11	
Interpret the product of a fraction and a whole number.						**5.NF.4.a** Topic 11	
Relate multiplication of fractions and the area of a rectangle with fractional side lengths.						**5.NF.4.b** Topic 11	
Interpret multiplication as scaling (resizing).						**5.NF.5** Topic 11	
Predict the size of a product compared to the size of one factor on the basis of the size of the other factor.						**5.NF.5.a** Topic 11	
Explain the effect of multiplying a given number by a fraction greater than 1, less than 1, or equal to 1.						**5.NF.5.b** Topic 11	
Solve real-world problems involving multiplication of fractions.						**5.NF.6** Topic 11	
Solve real-world problems involving multiplication of mixed numbers.						**5.NF.6** Topic 11	
Divide whole numbers and unit fractions.						**5.NF.7** Topic 11	
Interpret division of a unit fraction by a whole number.						**5.NF.7.a** Topic 11	
Interpret division of a whole number by a unit fraction.						**5.NF.7.b** Topic 11	
Solve real-world problems involving division of fractions and whole numbers.						**5.NF.7.c** Topic 11	

Domain **The Number System**

	K	1	2	3	4	5	6
Apply and extend previous understandings of multiplication and division to divide fractions by fractions.							
Divide fractions.							**6.NS.1** Topic 9
Solve word problems involving division of fractions by fractions.							**6.NS.1** Topic 9
Compute fluently with multi-digit numbers and find common factors and multiples.							
Fluently divide multi-digit numbers using the standard algorithm.							**6.NS.2** Topics 3, 4
Fluently add multi-digit decimals using the standard algorithm.							**6.NS.3** Topics 3, 6
Fluently subtract multi-digit decimals using the standard algorithm.							**6.NS.3** Topics 3, 6
Fluently multiply multi-digit decimals using the standard algorithm.							**6.NS.3** Topics 3, 6
Fluently divide decimals using the standard algorithm.							**6.NS.3** Topics 3, 6
Find the greatest common factor of two numbers.							**6.NS.4** Topic 5
Find the least common multiple of two numbers.							**6.NS.4** Topic 7
Use the distributive property.							**6.NS.4** Topic 5
Apply and extend previous understandings of numbers to the system of rational numbers.							
Interpret positive and negative numbers.							**6.NS.5** Topic 10
Show rational numbers on the number line.							**6.NS.6** Topics 9, 10
Show points on the number line with negative number coordinates.							**6.NS.6** Topic 10
Graph points with negative number coordinates.							**6.NS.6** Topic 10
Interpret opposites of numbers.							**6.NS.6.a** Topic 10
Relate signs of numbers in ordered pairs to quadrants of the coordinate plane.							**6.NS.6.b** Topic 10
Relate signs of numbers in ordered pairs to reflections in the coordinate plane.							**6.NS.6.b** Topic 10
Find and position integers on a horizontal or vertical number line.							**6.NS.6.c** Topic 10
Find and position pairs of integers on a coordinate plane.							**6.NS.6.c** Topic 10
Find and position pairs of rational numbers on a coordinate plane.							**6.NS.6.c** Topic 10
Order rational numbers.							**6.NS.7** Topic 10
Understand absolute value.							**6.NS.7** Topic 10
Relate inequalities to number lines.							**6.NS.7.a** Topic 10
Write, interpret, and explain ordering of rational numbers in real-world contexts.							**6.NS.7.b** Topic 10
Interpret the absolute value of a rational number.							**6.NS.7.c** Topic 10
Relate absolute value and order.							**6.NS.7.d** Topic 10
Graph points in the coordinate plane.							**6.NS.8** Topic 10
Find distances between points with the same first coordinate or the same second coordinate.							**6.NS.8** Topic 10

Domain Ratios and Proportional Relationships

	K	1	2	3	4	5	6
Understand ratio concepts and use ratio reasoning to solve problems.							
Understand and apply the concept of a ratio.							**6.RP.1** Topics 7, 12
Understand the concept of a unit rate.							**6.RP.2** Topics 12, 13
Use rate language.							**6.RP.2** Topics 12, 13
Solve problems involving ratios.							**6.RP.3** Topics 12–14
Solve problems involving rates.							**6.RP.3** Topics 12–14
Make tables of equivalent ratios.							**6.RP.3.a** Topic 13
Find missing values in tables of equivalent ratios.							**6.RP.3.a** Topic 13
On the coordinate plane, plot pairs of values given in tables of equivalent ratios.							**6.RP.3.a** Topic 13
Use tables to compare ratios.							**6.RP.3.a** Topic 13
Solve unit rate problems.							**6.RP.3.b** Topics 12, 13
Find a percent of a quantity.							**6.RP.3.c** Topic 14
Find the whole, given a part and the percent.							**6.RP.3.c** Topic 14
Convert measurement units.							**6.RP.3.d** Topic 16
Transform measurement units when multiplying or dividing quantities.							**6.RP.3.d** Topic 16

Domain **Measurement and Data**

	K	1	2	3	4	5	6
Describe and compare measurable attributes.							
Describe length as a measurable attribute of objects.	**K.MD.1** Topic 12						
Describe weight as a measurable attribute of objects.	**K.MD.1** Topic 12						
Describe several measurable attributes of a single object.	**K.MD.1** Topic 12						
Directly compare and describe two objects with a measurable attribute in common.	**K.MD.2** Topic 12						
Measure lengths indirectly and by iterating length units.							
Order three objects by length.		**1.MD.1** Topic 12					
Compare the lengths of two objects indirectly by using a third object.		**1.MD.1** Topic 12					
Understand and use length units.		**1.MD.2** Topic 12					
Measure and estimate lengths in standard units.							
Use rulers, yardsticks, meter sticks, and measuring tapes.			**2.MD.1** Topic 15				
Use and analyze different length units for the same object.			**2.MD.2** Topic 15				
Estimate lengths using inches or feet.			**2.MD.3** Topic 15				
Find how much longer one object is than another in standard units.			**2.MD.4** Topic 15				
Relate addition and subtraction to length.							
Use addition to solve word problems involving lengths.			**2.MD.5** Topic 15				
Use subtraction to solve word problems involving lengths.			**2.MD.5** Topic 15				
Represent whole numbers as lengths on a number line.			**2.MD.6** Topics 8, 9				
Show sums and differences within 100 on a number line.			**2.MD.6** Topics 8, 9				
Tell and write time.							
Tell and write time in hours.		**1.MD.3** Topic 13					
Tell and write time in half-hours.		**1.MD.3** Topic 13					
Work with time and money.							
Tell and write time to the nearest five minutes.			**2.MD.7** Topic 16				
Use a.m. and p.m.			**2.MD.7** Topic 16				
Solve word problems involving dollars and cents.			**2.MD.8** Topics 13, 14				
Use $ and ¢ symbols.			**2.MD.8** Topics 13, 14				
Solve problems involving measurement and estimation of intervals of time, liquid volumes, and masses of objects.							
Tell and write time to the nearest minute.				**3.MD.1** Topic 12			
Measure time intervals in minutes.				**3.MD.1** Topic 12			
Solve word problems involving addition and subtraction of time intervals in minutes.				**3.MD.1** Topic 12			

Domain **Measurement and Data** *cont.*

	K	1	2	3	4	5	6
Represent a time problem on a number line.				**3.MD.1** Topic 12			
Measure and estimate liquid volumes using standard units of liters (l).				**3.MD.2** Topic 15			
Solve one-step word problems involving liquid volumes.				**3.MD.2** Topic 15			
Solve problems involving measurement and conversion of measurements from a larger unit to a smaller unit.							
Know relative sizes of measurement units within one system of units.					**4.MD.1** Topic 14		
Know relative sizes of units of length.					**4.MD.1** Topic 14		
Know relative sizes of units of mass.					**4.MD.1** Topic 14		
Know relative sizes of units of weight.					**4.MD.1** Topic 14		
Know relative sizes of units of liquid volume.					**4.MD.1** Topic 14		
Know relative sizes of units of time.					**4.MD.1** Topic 14		
Convert from larger units to smaller units.					**4.MD.1** Topics 13, 14		
Make a table of measurement equivalents.					**4.MD.1** Topics 13, 14		
Solve word problems involving distances.					**4.MD.2** Topics 13–15		
Solve word problems involving intervals of time.					**4.MD.2** Topics 14, 15		
Solve word problems involving liquid volumes.					**4.MD.2** Topics 14, 15		
Solve word problems involving masses of objects.					**4.MD.2** Topics 14, 15		
Solve word problems involving money.					**4.MD.2** Topics 13–15		
Use the four operations to solve measurement word problems involving simple fractions.					**4.MD.2** Topics 13–15		
Represent measurement quantities on number line diagrams.					**4.MD.2** Topics 13–15		
Use the area formula for rectangles.					**4.MD.3** Topic 15		
Use the perimeter formula for rectangles.					**4.MD.3** Topic 15		
Convert like measurement units within a given measurement system.							
Convert measurement units.						**5.MD.1** Topic 13	
Use conversions to solve real-world problems.						**5.MD.1** Topic 13	
Geometric measurement: understand concepts of area and relate area to multiplication and to addition.							
Recognize area as an attribute of plane figures.				**3.MD.5** Topic 14			
Understand concepts of area measurement.				**3.MD.5** Topic 14			
Understand the concept of square unit.				**3.MD.5.a** Topic 14			
Relate *n* unit squares to an area of *n* square units.				**3.MD.5.b** Topic 14			
Measure areas by counting in square inches and feet.				**3.MD.6** Topic 14			

Domain **Measurement and Data** *cont.*

	K	1	2	3	4	5	6
Measure areas by counting unit squares in improvised units.				**3.MD.6** Topic 14			
Relate area to the operation of multiplication.				**3.MD.7** Topic 14			
Relate area to the operation of addition.				**3.MD.7** Topic 14			
Find the area of a rectangle by tiling it.				**3.MD.7.a** Topic 14			
Show that the area of a rectangle can be found by multiplying the side lengths.				**3.MD.7.a** Topic 14			
Multiply side lengths to find areas of rectangles.				**3.MD.7.b** Topic 14			
Represent whole-number products as rectangular areas in mathematical reasoning.				**3.MD.7.b** Topic 14			
Use tiling to show that the area of a rectangle with side lengths a and $b + c$ is the sum of $a \times b$ and $a \times c$.				**3.MD.7.c** Topics 6, 14			
Use area models to represent the distributive property.				**3.MD.7.c** Topic 14			
Find areas of rectilinear figures by decomposing them into non-overlapping rectangles.				**3.MD.7.d** Topics 6, 14			
Geometric measurement: recognize perimeter as an attribute of plane figures and distinguish between linear and area measures.							
Solve perimeter problems.				**3.MD.8** Topics 6, 13, 14			
Solve perimeter problems involving finding an unknown side length.				**3.MD.8** Topic 13			
Exhibit rectangles with the same perimeter and different areas.				**3.MD.8** Topic 13			
Exhibit rectangles with the same area and different perimeters.				**3.MD.8** Topic 14			
Geometric measurement: understand concepts of angle and measure angles.							
Understand how angles are formed.					**4.MD.5** Topic 16		
Understand concepts of angle measurement.					**4.MD.5** Topic 16		
Relate angle measurement in degrees to circles.					**4.MD.5.a** Topic 16		
Relate one-degree angles to n-degree angles.					**4.MD.5.b** Topic 16		
Measure angles using a protractor.					**4.MD.6** Topic 16		
Sketch angles of specified measure.					**4.MD.6** Topic 16		
Recognize angle measure as additive.					**4.MD.7** Topic 16		
Solve addition and subtraction problems to find unknown angles on a diagram.					**4.MD.7** Topic 16		
Geometric measurement: understand concepts of volume and relate volume to multiplication and to addition.							
Recognize volume as an attribute of solid figures.						**5.MD.3** Topic 12	
Understand concepts of volume measurement.						**5.MD.3** Topic 12	
Understand the concept of cubic unit.						**5.MD.3.a** Topic 12	
Relate n unit cubes to a volume of n cubic units.						**5.MD.3.b** Topic 12	

Domain **Measurement and Data** *cont.*

	K	1	2	3	4	5	6
Measure volumes by counting in cubic inches and feet.						**5.MD.4** Topic 12	
Measure volumes by counting unit cubes in improvised units.						**5.MD.4** Topic 12	
Relate volume to the operations of multiplication and addition.						**5.MD.5** Topic 12	
Solve real-world and mathematical problems involving volume.						**5.MD.5** Topic 12	
Show that the volume of a right rectangular prism can be found by multiplying the edge lengths.						**5.MD.5.a** Topic 12	
Show that the volume of a right rectangular prism can be found by multiplying the height by the area of the base.						**5.MD.5.a** Topic 12	
Represent threefold whole-number products as volumes.						**5.MD.5.a** Topic 12	
Use the formulas $V = \ell \times w \times h$ and $V = b \times h$ for rectangular prisms.						**5.MD.5.b** Topic 12	
Find volumes of solid figures composed of two non-overlapping right rectangular prisms.						**5.MD.5.c** Topic 12	
Classify objects and count the number of objects in each category.							
Classify objects into given categories.	**K.MD.3** Topics 9, 13						
Count the numbers of objects in a category.	**K.MD.3** Topics 9, 13						
Sort categories by count.	**K.MD.3** Topics 9, 13						
Represent and interpret data.							
Organize, represent, interpret, and compare data with up to three categories.		**1.MD.4** Topic 14					
Measure objects to generate whole-number length data.			**2.MD.9** Topic 16				
Make repeated measurements of the same object to generate length data.			**2.MD.9** Topic 16				
Draw a picture graph to represent a data set with up to four categories.			**2.MD.10** Topic 16				
Draw a bar graph with up to four categories.			**2.MD.10** Topic 16				
Solve problems using data presented in a bar graph.			**2.MD.10** Topic 16				
Draw a scaled picture graph to represent a data set with several categories.				**3.MD.3** Topic 16			
Draw a scaled bar graph to represent a data set with several categories.				**3.MD.3** Topic 16			
Solve problems using information presented in scaled bar graphs.				**3.MD.3** Topic 16			
Find lengths involving halves and fourths of a unit and display them in a line plot.				**3.MD.4** Topic 16			
Solve problems involving addition and subtraction of fractions by using measurement data in line plots.					**4.MD.4** Topic 15		
Make a line plot to display measurements involving halves, fourths, and eighths of a unit.					**4.MD.4** Topic 15		
Solve problems involving fraction operations by using measurement data in line plots.						**5.MD.2** Topic 14	

Domain Statistics and Probability

	K	1	2	3	4	5	6
Develop understanding of statistical variability.							
Understand statistical questions.							6.SP.1 Topic 19
Understand how data are described by a measure of center.							6.SP.2 Topic 19
Understand how data are described by their spread.							6.SP.2 Topic 19
Understand how data are described by the overall shape.							6.SP.2 Topic 19
Understand how a measure of center describes the data values.							6.SP.3 Topic 19
Understand how a measure of variability describes how the data values in a set vary.							6.SP.3 Topic 19
Summarize and describe distributions.							
Display numerical data in plots on a number line.							6.SP.4 Topic 19
Display numerical data in dot plots.							6.SP.4 Topic 19
Display numerical data in histograms.							6.SP.4 Topic 19
Display numerical data in box plots.							6.SP.4 Topic 19
Summarize numerical data in relation to their context.							6.SP.5 Topic 19
For numerical data, report the number of observations.							6.SP.5.a Topic 19
For numerical data, describe the nature of the attribute under investigation.							6.SP.5.b Topic 19
For numerical data, describe how the investigated attribute was measured and its units of measurement.							6.SP.5.b Topic 19
Find the median of a set of data.							6.SP.5.c Topic 19
Find the mean of a set of data.							6.SP.5.c Topic 19
Find the interquartile range and/or mean absolute deviation of a data set.							6.SP.5.c Topic 19
Describe overall patterns or deviations in a data set.							6.SP.5.c Topic 19
Relate a measure of center to the shape of the data distribution and context of data collection.							6.SP.5.d Topic 19
Relate a measure of variability to the shape of the data distribution and context of data collection.							6.SP.5.d Topic 19

Domain **Geometry**

	K	1	2	3	4	5	6
Identify and describe shapes (squares, circles, triangles, rectangles, hexagons, cubes, cones, cylinders, and spheres).							
Describe shapes in the environment.	**K.G.1** Topic 15						
Describe position.	**K.G.1** Topic 15						
Correctly name shapes regardless of their orientations.	**K.G.2** Topics 14, 16						
Correctly name shapes regardless of their overall size.	**K.G.2** Topics 14, 16						
Identify two-dimensional shapes as flat.	**K.G.3** Topics 14, 16						
Identify three-dimensional shapes as solid.	**K.G.3** Topics 14, 16						
Analyze, compare, create, and compose shapes.							
Analyze and compare two- and three-dimensional shapes in different sizes.	**K.G.4** Topic 16						
Analyze and compare two- and three-dimensional shapes in different orientations.	**K.G.4** Topic 16						
Build and draw shapes to model shapes in the world.	**K.G.5** Topic 16						
Compose simple shapes to form larger shapes.	**K.G.6** Topic 16						
Reason with shapes and their attributes.							
Distinguish between defining attributes versus non-defining attributes.		**1.G.1** Topic 15					
Build and draw shapes with defining attributes.		**1.G.1** Topic 15					
Compose two- and three-dimensional shapes.		**1.G.2** Topic 15					
Compose new shapes from composite shapes.		**1.G.2** Topic 15					
Partition circles and rectangles into two equal shares and use related vocabulary.		**1.G.3** Topic 16					
Partition circles and rectangles into four equal shares and use related vocabulary.		**1.G.3** Topic 16					
Recognize that decomposing shapes into more equal shares creates smaller shares.		**1.G.3** Topic 16					
Recognize and draw two- and three-dimensional shapes having specified attributes.			**2.G.1** Topic 12				
Identify triangles, quadrilaterals, pentagons, hexagons, and cubes.			**2.G.1** Topic 12				
Partition a rectangle into rows and columns of same-size squares and count the squares.			**2.G.2** Topic 12				
Partition circles and rectangles into two, three, or four equal shares, and use related vocabulary.			**2.G.3** Topic 12				
Recognize that equal shares of identical wholes need not have the same shape.			**2.G.3** Topic 12				
Understand that shapes in different categories may share attributes.				**3.G.1** Topic 11			
Understand that shared attributes of shapes can define a larger category.				**3.G.1** Topic 11			
Recognize rhombuses, rectangles, and squares as examples of quadrilaterals and draw quadrilaterals that are non-examples.				**3.G.1** Topic 11			
Partition shapes into parts with equal areas.				**3.G.2** Topics 11, 14			
Express the area of each equal part of a shape as a unit fraction of the whole.				**3.G.2** Topics 11, 14			

Domain **Geometry** *cont.*

	K	1	2	3	4	5	6
Draw and identify lines and angles, and classify shapes by properties of their lines and angles.							
Draw and identify points, lines, line segments, and rays.					4.G.1 Topic 16		
Draw and identify parallel and perpendicular lines.					4.G.1 Topic 16		
Draw and identify angles.					4.G.1 Topic 16		
Draw and identify right, acute, and obtuse angles.					4.G.1 Topic 16		
Use parallel or perpendicular lines to classify figures.					4.G.2 Topic 16		
Use angle measure to classify figures.					4.G.2 Topic 16		
Categorize and identify right triangles.					4.G.2 Topic 16		
Understand line symmetry.					4.G.3 Topic 16		
Identify line-symmetric figures.					4.G.3 Topic 16		
Draw lines of symmetry.					4.G.3 Topic 16		
Classify two-dimensional figures into categories based on their properties.							
Understand that attributes belonging to a category of two-dimensional figures also belong to all subcategories of that category.						5.G.3 Topic 15	
Classify two-dimensional figures in a hierarchy based on properties.						5.G.4 Topic 15	
Graph points on the coordinate plane to solve real-world and mathematical problems.							
Understand a coordinate system.						5.G.1 Topic 16	
Graph points in the first quadrant of the coordinate plane.						5.G.2 Topic 16	
Interpret coordinate values of points in the first quadrant of the coordinate plane.						5.G.2 Topic 16	
Solve real-world and mathematical problems involving area, surface area, and volume.							
Find area by composing a figure into rectangles.							6.G.1 Topics 8, 11, 17
Find area by decomposing a figure into triangles and other shapes.							6.G.1 Topics 8, 11, 17
Find the volume of a right rectangular prism with fractional edge lengths by packing it with unit cubes of the appropriate unit fraction edge lengths.							6.G.2 Topic 18
Show that the volume of a right rectangular prism with fractional edge lengths can be found by multiplying the edge lengths of the prism.							6.G.2 Topic 18
Apply the formulas $V = \ell\,w\,h$ and $V = b\,h$ to find volumes of right rectangular prisms with fractional edge lengths.							6.G.2 Topic 18
Draw polygons in the coordinate plane.							6.G.3 Topics 10, 11
Find the length of a side of a polygon drawn in the coordinate plane.							6.G.3 Topic 11
Represent three-dimensional figures using nets.							6.G.4 Topics 17, 18
Use nets to find the surface area of three-dimensional figures.							6.G.4 Topic 18

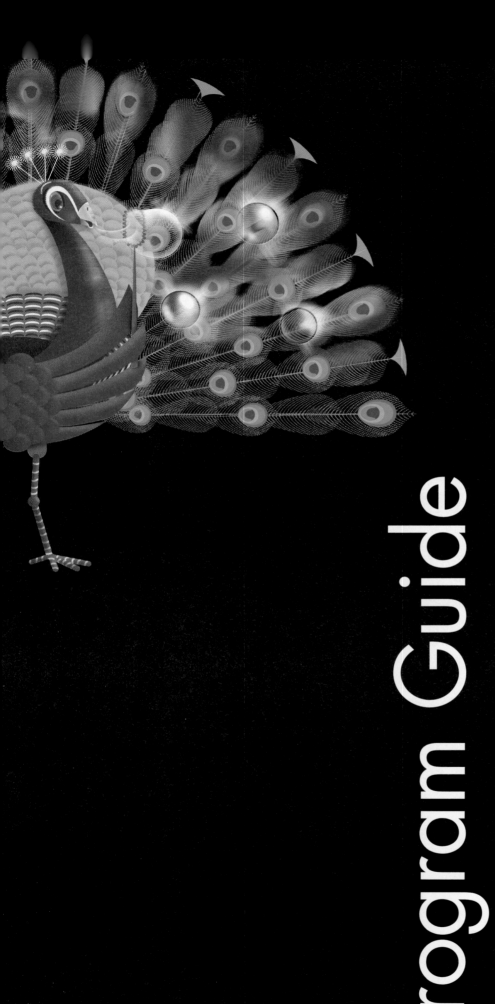

Program Guide

Concepts and Problem Solving

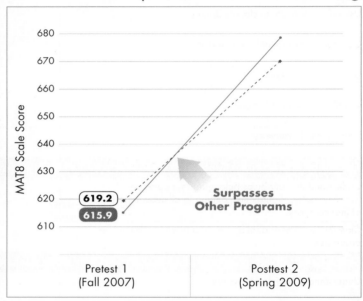

enVisionMATH

Control

Better Conceptual Understanding and Problem Solving

enVisionMATH students were UNSURPASSED in conceptual understanding and problem solving, despite starting out at a lower level.

The difference shown in this graph is statistically significant.

Statistically More Effective

Pearson authorship team conducts a thorough review of scientific research to determine new educational practices.

Computation

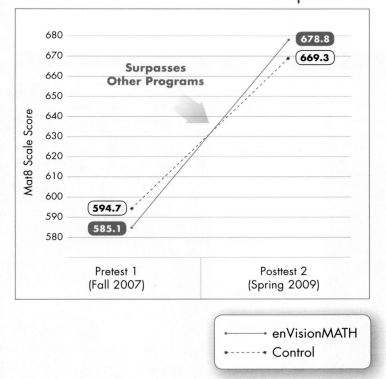

Ability Level

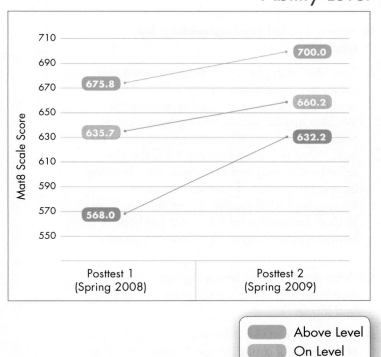

Better Computation Scores

enVisionMATH students were UNSURPASSED in computational skills, despite starting out at a lower math level.

The difference shown in this graph is statistically significant.

Better Results for All Ability Levels

All ability levels increased in mathematical achievement using *enVisionMATH*.

Low-level students showed the most gain, indicating a narrowing of the "achievement gap."

The difference shown in this graph is statistically significant.

A Conversation with Grant Wiggins

Q What is Understanding by Design?

A **Understanding by Design** is a comprehensive approach to unit planning, and a series of resources on curricular planning developed by Grant Wiggins and Jay McTighe and published by the Association for Supervision and Curriculum Development (ASCD).

Q Why is it called **Understanding by Design?**

A Consider each phrase: as educators, we aim for student *understanding,* not merely the acquisition of superficial skill or knowledge. We also aim for understanding by design as opposed to having it happen by chance or by luck. What is "understanding"? It is the ability to make meaning and to transfer prior learning to new tasks. Well, if you want those two things—and what teacher doesn't?—you have to plan and design for it and not just hope it happens as an outgrowth of learning content.

Q What do you mean by saying that understanding is two things: *meaning making* and *transfer?*

A Well, those are two different, yet related parts of the word. If a student can "connect the dots" or "see patterns" or "make inferences" that go beyond the particulars, then we all agree that the student really "understands." But we also say that if a student can't apply or transfer prior learning to new and perhaps unfamiliar situations and tasks, then the student really doesn't "understand."

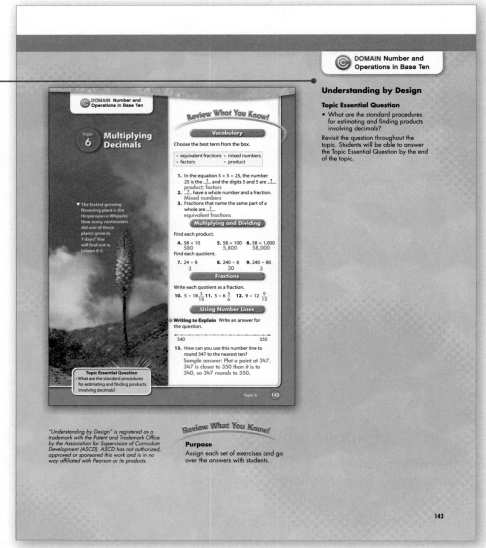

"Understanding by Design" is registered as a trademark with the Patent and Trademark Office by the Association for Supervision of Curriculum Development (ASCD). ASCD has not authorized, approved or sponsored this work and is in no way affiliated with Pearson or its products.

▲ **Teacher's Edition**

Q Where in *enVisionMATH Common Core* are Understanding by Design principles implemented?

A *enVisionMATH Common Core* includes Understanding by Design in every

- Topic Math Background
- Topic Opener
- Lesson Overview
- Lesson Close

Q Why is Understanding by Design needed?

A To make sure that all students develop understanding, you have to deliberately and purposefully target students' abilities to ask questions, make connections, and transfer their prior learning to new tasks. Doing so requires a more explicit plan where you design "backward" from understanding—meaning making and transference—instead of "backward" from content mastery.

Q How important is "understanding" in beginning math instruction? Isn't the point just to make sure students learn the key skills?

A This is a vital issue that educators may not think through sufficiently. Skill, by itself, does not answer the question, *How and when should I use each skill?* Answering that question requires understanding. Skill and knowledge by themselves do not help students solve new and unfamiliar-looking problems.

Problem solving requires applying learning to new and unfamiliar tasks. It is like literacy instruction: students need to know what to do when they get stuck or puzzled if they are going to be successful users of mathematics skills.

Q So math is not just skills and facts?

A No, there are some big ideas that can help students make sense of everything they do and make it more likely that they can solve new problems. Here is a big idea about problem solving: *Problem solving is turning unknowns into knowns and unfamiliars into familiars, by means of helpful equivalences.* That's the point of learning to factor, regroup, or any simplifying techniques. These techniques also help students realize, slowly but surely, what the equal sign really means.

> *" … there are some big ideas that can help students make sense of everything they do and make it more likely that they can solve new problems. "*

Once students understand this idea — that is, they make it a key strategy—then they will "see" the skill work differently, with greater perspective. They will better understand the value of each new skill and be more likely to transfer their learning to new problems.

Q So, is this where big questions can be found in math— questions about problem solving?

A That's one key area for big questions: For example, *What kind of problem is this? What does it remind me of? What is the problem really asking, even if it doesn't say so directly?*—these are all big questions. They start out being the teacher's questions; but they have to end up, over time, being the students' questions if understanding is to occur.

Through visual learning, students make sense of problems, develop solutions to plans, and use tools appropriately, all leading to conceptual understanding.

WorldScapes®

Research says nonfiction literature is an effective way to reinforce real-world problem solving and applications (Dreher, 2000).

enVisionMATH Common Core references **WorldScapes® math content readers** which:

- **Are beautiful nonfiction books** that include passages about real-world math along with comprehension questions.

- **Provide cross-cultural, cross-curricular** literacy resources that interweave math skills and concepts with facts about the history, environment, and culture of specific countries.

- **Offer engaging contexts** that include interesting information with appealing pictures. A child from each country introduces the book and poses questions about the main topic.

- **Are referenced** in each topic on The Language of Math page in the Teacher's Edition.

- **Are useful** in developing intervention strategies and in providing differentiated instruction opportunities.

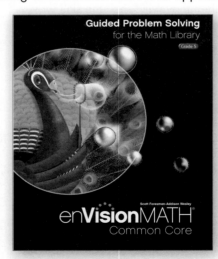

- Packaged with **Guided Problem-Solving Masters** and teacher notes.

- Support the **Common Core State Standards** by addressing the goals of the **Mathematical Practices**. Pictures allow students to discern patterns, see and make use of structure, and simplify complex situations.

Fabulous Fiji

Fiji is an archipelago (AR kuh PEL uh go) in the Pacific Ocean. It has 322 islands that are large enough for people to live on, but only 106 islands actually have people living on them. Fiji has a population of more than 800,000 people. Almost nine-tenths of Fijians live on the two largest islands.

Viti Levu, the main island of Fiji, is home to seven-tenths of the population.

archipelago   a large body of water with many islands

4

▲ **WorldScapes Math Content Readers**

Fiji is a popular place for vacations. There are direct flights to Fiji from New Zealand and other countries around the rim of the Pacific Ocean.

Distances from Fiji (Miles)

CANADA
Vancouver

JAPAN
Tokyo

UNITED STATES OF AMERICA

Los Angeles

Honolulu

5,871

5,524

3,166

4,428

With a partner, take turns picking a distance on the map and reading it aloud. Then write the distances in order, from least to greatest.

AUSTRALIA
Sydney
Melbourne

FIJI

1,961
2,395
1,328

Auckland

NEW ZEALAND

5

Arctic

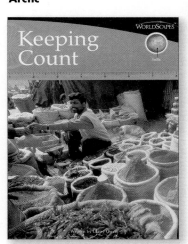

India

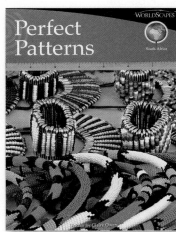

South Africa

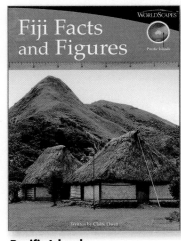

Pacific Islands

China

Costa Rica

Australia

Problem Solving

Research says that for all content areas, conceptual understanding, computational fluency, and problem-solving skills are each essential and mutually reinforcing, influencing performance on such varied tasks as estimation, word problems, and computation (National Mathematics Advisory Panel, 2008).

enVisionMATH Common Core provides:

- **Problem-solving skills and strategies** taught in problem-solving lessons.

- **Phases in a problem-solving process** taught in problem-solving lessons. The phases are: Read and Understand, Plan and Solve, and Look Back and Check.

- **Problem-Based Interactive Learning** that supports teaching through problem solving.

- **Problems in examples** to reinforce meanings of operations.

- **A variety of problem-solving exercises** including: Think About the Structure, Reasonableness, Writing to Explain, Use Tools, and Write a Problem.

- **Problem-Solving Handbook** in front of the student book that students can go back to during the year.

- **Problem-Solving Recording Sheet** that helps students record their thinking.

- **Mixed Problem Solving** pages for more reinforcement of choosing strategies.

> *A new approach to solving word problems is to use bar diagrams as visual representations that show how quantities in a word problem are related.*
>
> —Dr. Randall Charles

The Standards for Mathematical Practice stress the importance of strong problem-solving and reasoning abilities to develop conceptual understanding.

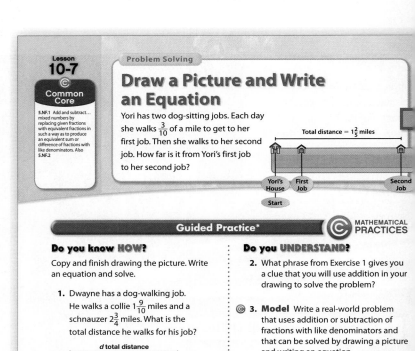

▲ **Student Edition**

Left page (partial)

Read and Understand

What do I know?
Yori walks $\frac{3}{10}$ of a mile to her first job. At her second job she will have walked a total of $1\frac{2}{5}$ miles.

What am I asked to find?
The distance from the first to the second job

Plan and Solve

Draw a Picture

$1\frac{2}{5}$ miles

$\frac{3}{10}$	d miles

Write an Equation
Let d = the distance from first to second job

$\frac{3}{10} + d = 1\frac{2}{5}$ or $1\frac{2}{5} - \frac{3}{10} = d$

$1\frac{2}{5} - \frac{3}{10} = 1\frac{4}{10} - \frac{3}{10} = 1\frac{1}{10}$

$d = 1\frac{1}{10}$ miles

It is $1\frac{1}{10}$ miles from Yori's first job to her second job.

---

6. Renee mixed red, white, and yellow paint. She used $1\frac{2}{3}$ gallons of red paint, $5\frac{5}{6}$ gallons of white paint, and $2\frac{1}{2}$ gallons of yellow. How many gallons of paint did Renee mix in all?

7. Katya needs $2\frac{5}{6}$ yards of satin fabric. She has $\frac{3}{4}$ of a yard now. How much more fabric does Katya need to buy?

8. Look for Patterns Give an example of when the sum of two fractions equals 1 whole.

9. Parker's dad drove $2\frac{1}{3}$ miles from the start of a construction zone. He stopped to read this road sign. How far will Parker's dad have driven when he reaches the end of the construction zone?

End of
Construction
$1\frac{3}{4}$ mi

10. Critique Reasoning Gene says that the two circles below show the same amount. Do you agree? Write a good math explanation to support your decision.

11. Communicate In many cases, a baby's weight at birth is equal to one half his or her weight at age one. Explain how to estimate the weight of a baby at birth if this baby weighs 18 pounds at age one.

12.

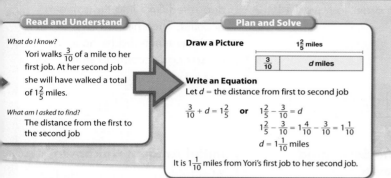

...eaf pine sapling
How many feet

D $3\frac{3}{12}$ feet

Lesson 10-7   267

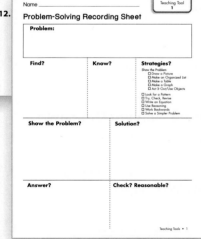

▲ **Problem-Solving Recording Sheet**

Bar Diagrams

Research says that bar diagrams help students understand the relationships between quantities in a problem, and this helps students choose a correct operation to solve the problem (Diezmann and English, 2001).

enVisionMATH Common Core provides:

- **Visual models for ways to make a number in Grade K** to build a foundation for addition and subtraction.

8 is 3 and 5.   8 is 4 and 4.

- **Visual models for addition and subtraction situations in Grades 1–2** to help children see relationships between quantities. In the model, children place objects, then later draw dots, and then later write numbers.

Joining

There are 3 birds. 2 more fly in. How many in all?

There are 3 birds. More fly in. Then there are 5 in all. How many flew in?

There are some birds. 2 more fly in. Then there are 5 in all. How many were there to begin with?

Separating

There are 7 birds. 3 birds fly away. How many are left?

There are 7 birds. Some fly away. Then 4 birds are left. How many flew away?

There are some birds. 3 birds fly away. Then 4 birds are left. How many were there to begin with?

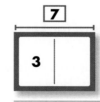

The models help children think about joining and separating as **Part-Part-Whole**. Children add when the whole is unknown and subtract when a part is unknown. Comparison problems and joining-equal groups problems are also introduced.

Bar Diagrams: Addition-Subtraction

Joining

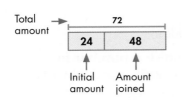

Total amount → 72
| 24 | 48 |

↑ Initial amount ↑ Amount joined

Total Amount Unknown

Kim has 23 dolls. Her father gives her 18 more dolls. Now how many dolls does she have?

?
| 23 | 18 |

Amount Joined Unknown

Debbie has saved $57. How much more money does she need in order to have $112?

112
| 57 | ? |

Initial Amount Unknown

Tom had some money in his savings account. He then deposited $45 into the same account. Then he had $92 in all. How much did he have in his savings account to start?

92
| ? | 45 |

Separating

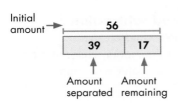

Initial amount → 56
| 39 | 17 |

↑ Amount separated ↑ Amount remaining

Amount Remaining Unknown

Steven had 122 peanuts. He ate 71 of them. How many peanuts are left?

122
| 71 | ? |

Amount Separated Unknown

Carrie had 45 CDs. She gave some to Jo. Then Carrie had 27 left. How many did she give to Jo?

45
| ? | 27 |

Initial Amount Unknown

Alan had some marbles. He lost 12 of them. Then he had 32 left. How many did he have to begin with?

?
| 12 | 32 |

Part-Part-Whole

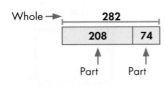

Whole → 282
| 208 | 74 |

↑ Part ↑ Part

Whole Unknown

A kennel has 14 cats and 16 dogs. How many dogs and cats are in the kennel?

?
| 14 | 16 |

One Part Unknown

Jim has 18 wheat crackers and some rye crackers. He has 63 crackers in all. How many rye crackers does he have?

63
| 18 | ? |

Another Part Unknown

Some adults and 12 children are on a bus. There are 31 people on the bus. How many adults are on the bus?

31
| ? | 12 |

Joining and separating can be thought of as part-part-whole. You can add when the whole is unknown. You can subtract when a part is unknown.

Comparison

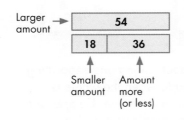

Larger amount →
| 54 |
| 18 | 36 |

↑ Smaller amount ↑ Amount more (or less)

Amount More (or Less) Unknown

Alex has 47 toy cars. Keisha has 12 toy cars. How many more cars does Alex have?

47
| 12 | ? |

Smaller Amount Unknown

Fran spent $84 which was $26 more than Alice spent. How much did Alice spend?

84
| ? | 26 |

Larger Amount Unknown

Barney has 23 old coins. Steve has 16 more old coins than Barney. How many old coins does Steve have?

?
| 23 | 16 |

You can add when the larger amount is unknown. You can subtract when the smaller amount or the amount more (or the amount less) is unknown.

Bar Diagrams: Multiplication-Division

Joining Equal Groups

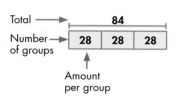

Total Amount Unknown

Kim has 4 photo albums. Each album has 85 pictures. How many photos are in her 4 albums?

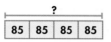

Amount Per Group Unknown

Pam put the same number of apples in each of 4 bags. She ended up with 52 apples in bags. How many apples did she put in each bag?

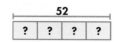

Number of Groups Unknown

Fred bought some books. Each book cost $16. He spent $80 on books. How many books did he buy?

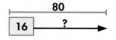

Separating Equal Groups

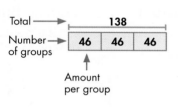

Amount Per Group Unknown

Bryan got 45 pigeons. He put them in 5 pens with the same number of pigeons in each pen. How many pigeons are in each pen?

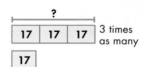

Number of Groups Unknown

A total of 108 children signed up for soccer. The coach put them into 18-person teams. How many teams were made?

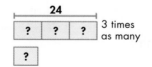

Total Amount Unknown

Kim had some cards. She put them into piles of 35 and was able to make 4 piles. How many cards did she start with?

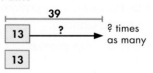

Joining or separating equal groups is like part-part-whole. You can multiply when a whole (total) is unknown. You can divide when the number of equal parts (groups) or the size of each part group is unknown.

Comparison

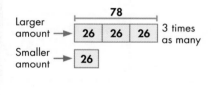

Larger Amount Unknown

Alex has 17 toy cars, Keisha has 3 times as many. How many cars does Keisha have?

Smaller Amount Unknown

Barney has 24 old coins. This is 3 times as many coins as Steve has. How many old coins does Steve have?

Number of Times as Many Unknown

Ann's teacher is 39 years old. Ann is 13 years old. Ann's teacher is how many times as old as Ann?

You can multiply when the larger amount is unknown. You can divide when the smaller amount or the number of times as many is unknown.

- **Focused instruction on bar diagrams** is in problem-solving lessons, in lessons on meanings of operations, and in lessons on mental math.
- **A variety of problems** as shown here are infused in lessons to help students develop the quantitative reasoning needed for success on high-stakes tests and in real life.

Algebra in Kindergarten Through Grade 6

Research says that rule-based instructional approaches that do not give students opportunities to create meaning for the rules or to learn when to use them can lead to forgetting, unsystematic errors, reliance on visual clues, and poor strategic decisions. (Mathematics Learning Study Committee, 2001)

"To prepare students for Algebra, the curriculum must simultaneously develop conceptual understanding, computational fluency, and problem-solving skills. These three aspects of learning are mutually reinforcing and should not be seen as competing for class time" (National Mathematics Advisory Panel, 2008, p. 19).

The National Mathematics Advisory Panel proposed three clusters of concepts and skills that serve as the Critical Foundation of Algebra:

(1) fluency with whole numbers,

(2) fluency with fractions, and

(3) particular aspects of geometry and measurement.

Students in Kindergarten through Grade 6 can develop the algebraic thinking skills by using **patterns** to make **generalizations,** and by using **mathematical symbols** to describe **relationships.**

enVisionMATH Common Core provides:

• lessons involving patterns and generalizations.

• multiple representations of relationships.

Kindergarten Visual Learning Bridge

Grade 1 Visual Learning Bridge

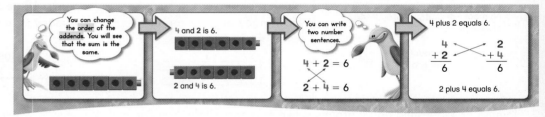

Grade 2 Visual Learning Bridge

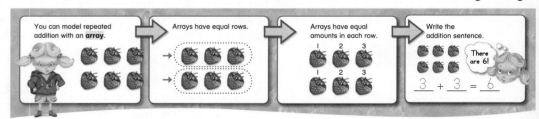

Grade 3 Visual Learning Bridge

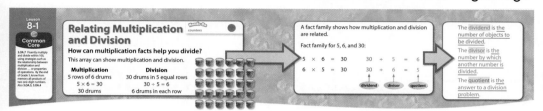

Grade 4 Visual Learning Bridge

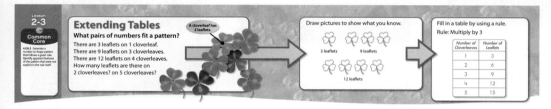

Grade 5 Visual Learning Bridge

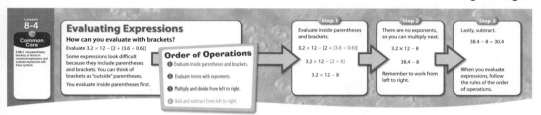

Grade 6 Visual Learning Bridge

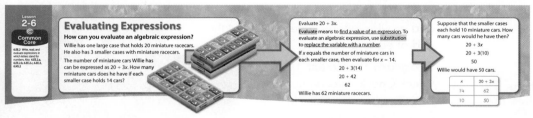

Patterns and Functions

- **Extending Repeating Patterns**
  Circle the shape that comes next.

- **Using Rules for Patterns**
  Use your rule to continue the pattern.
  38, 32, 26, 20, ▮, ▮

  Complete the table and find a rule.

d	12	14	20	26
$d +$ ▮	25	27	33	▮

Properties and Operations

- **Applying Properties**
  Write the sum. Change the order of the addends.
  2 + 5 = ___   ___ + ___ = ___

- **Using Inverse Operations**
  Find the number that makes both sentences true.
  ▮ × 6 = 42   42 ÷ 6 = ▮

- **Using Order of Operations**
  Evaluate the expression.
  27 ÷ (5 + 4) + 52

Equations and Expressions

- **Finding Missing Numbers**
  7 + 5 = 9 + ___

- **Writing Expressions**
  Write an algebraic expression for the word phrase. Let x represent the number.
  four less than a number times six.

- **Solving Equations**
  $m + 41 = 95$

- **Listing Solution Pairs**
  Use the equation to complete the table.
  $b = \dfrac{a}{4} - 1$

a	4	8	10	12	16
b					

Equivalence: Equality/Inequality

- **Checking For Equivalence**
  Tell if the equation is true or false.
  36 ÷ 4 = 3 × 3 × 3

- **Comparing Quantities**
  Use >, <, or = for ◯.   −8 ◯ −12

Frequent Progress Monitoring

enVisionMath Common Core provides frequent assessment opportunities as shown in the white boxes in the flowchart below.

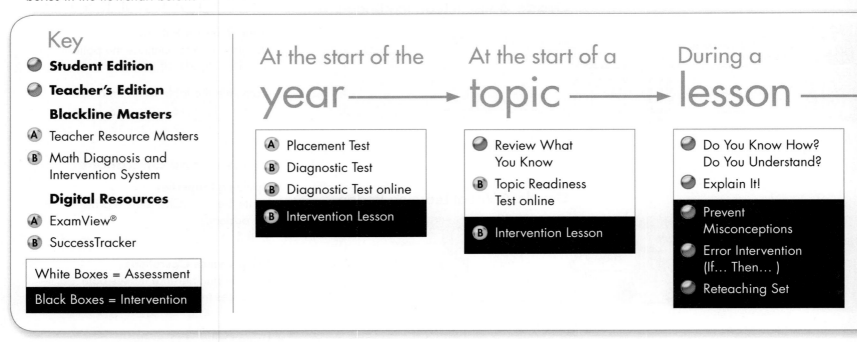

Key

- 🔵 **Student Edition**
- 🟢 **Teacher's Edition**

Blackline Masters

- Ⓐ Teacher Resource Masters
- Ⓑ Math Diagnosis and Intervention System

Digital Resources

- Ⓐ ExamView®
- Ⓑ SuccessTracker

| White Boxes = Assessment |
| Black Boxes = Intervention |

At the start of the year ⟶ **At the start of a topic** ⟶ **During a lesson** ⟶

- Ⓐ Placement Test
- Ⓑ Diagnostic Test
- Ⓑ Diagnostic Test online
- Ⓑ Intervention Lesson

- 🔵 Review What You Know
- Ⓑ Topic Readiness Test online
- Ⓑ Intervention Lesson

- 🔵 Do You Know How? Do You Understand?
- 🟢 Explain It!
- 🟢 Prevent Misconceptions
- 🟢 Error Intervention (If… Then…)
- 🟢 Reteaching Set

Response to Intervention (RTI)

enVisionMATH Common Core provides solid and effective intervention that makes it easy for teachers to respond to students' individual needs.

RTI Ⓐ TIER 1 — Ongoing Intervention

Monitor Progress and prevent misconceptions during core lesson instruction.

Program features: Prevent Misconceptions, Error Intervention

Error Intervention

If students give incorrect products becau[se] the 4s facts,

then review the doubling strategy for 4s 18 on the board and ask: *How can you u[se]* *product of 9 × 4?* [Double the product of the 2s fact. 9 × 4 = 18 + 18 = 36.] *Suppose that you want to multiply 6 × 4.* Write 6 × 4 on the board. *How can you use a 2s fact to find the product?* [You know 6 × 2 = 12, so double the product: 6 × 4 = 12 + 12 = 24.]

Preventing Misconceptions
Remind students that these methods of multiplying with 8 are strategies for helping to find the product. Point out that they are using facts they already know to help them with new facts.

RTI Ⓑ TIER 2 — Strategic Intervention

Identify students' strengths and needs and provide appropriate support at the end of each lesson.

Program features:
Quick Check, Intervention Activities, Center Activities, Reteaching Masters

Math Diagnosis and Intervention System for end-of-topic assessment, reteaching, and enrichment

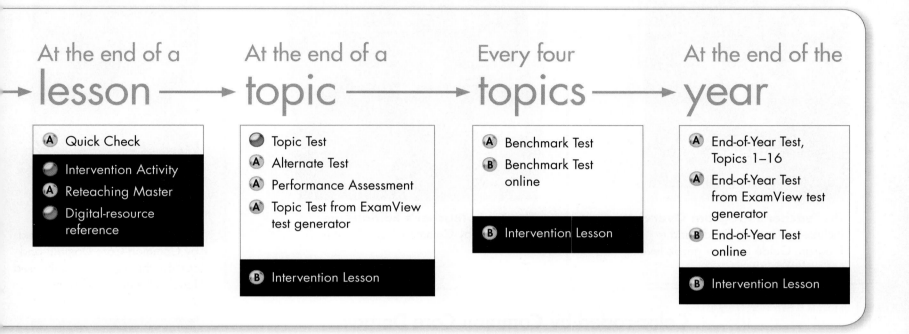

At the end of a **lesson** →	At the end of a **topic** →	Every four **topics** →	At the end of the **year**
(A) Quick Check	(●) Topic Test	(A) Benchmark Test	(A) End-of-Year Test, Topics 1–16
(●) Intervention Activity	(A) Alternate Test	(B) Benchmark Test online	(A) End-of-Year Test from ExamView test generator
(A) Reteaching Master	(A) Performance Assessment	(B) Intervention Lesson	(B) End-of-Year Test online
(●) Digital-resource reference	(A) Topic Test from ExamView test generator		(B) Intervention Lesson
	(B) Intervention Lesson		

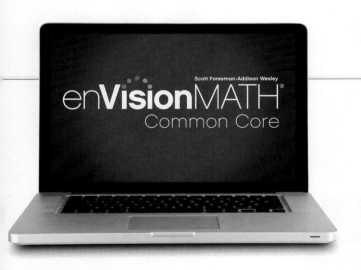

Digital System

- Diagnose students' understanding of the Common Core State Standards automatically.
- Prescribe personalized instruction based on student performance.

RTI **Intensive** Intervention

Provide more intense personalized instruction for students who continue to struggle.

focusMATH

- Focus on foundational math skills— intensive, balanced and individualized
- Explicit instruction and stepped-out math models
- Each unit based on a specific NCTM focal point
- Systematic Assessment plans

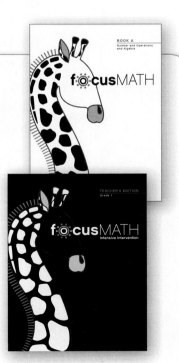

Components Organized the Way You Teach

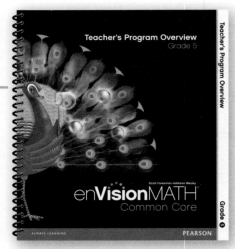

The **Teacher's Program Overview** includes a Content Guide and a Program Guide for your grade level.

The **Topic Teacher's Editions** are organized by Common Core Domains.

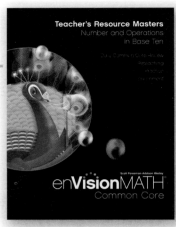

The **Teacher's Resource Masters** books are organized by Common Core Domain and contain the most frequently used Teacher Resource Masters.

Color-coded by Common Core Domains

- **Counting and Cardinality** (Grade K)
- **Operations and Algebraic Thinking** (Grades K–5)
- **Expressions and Equations** (Grade 6)
- **Number and Operations in Base Ten** (Grades K–5)
- **Number and Operations—Fractions** (Grades 3–5)
- **The Number System** (Grade 6)
- **Ratios and Proportional Relationships** (Grade 6)
- **Measurement and Data** (Grades K–5)
- **Statistics and Probability** (Grade 6)
- **Geometry** (Grades K–6)

Student Edition

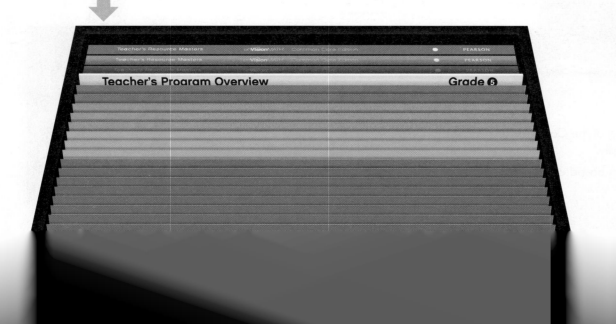

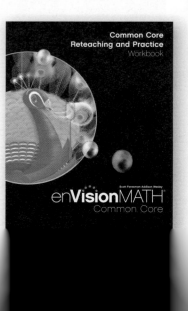

Instruction for All Learners

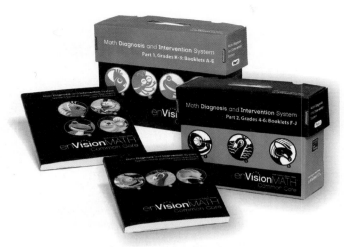

Ready-Made Center for Differentiated Instruction

Math Diagnosis and Intervention System

focusMATH

Math Literature

Interactive Math Stories Big Book
(Grades K–2)

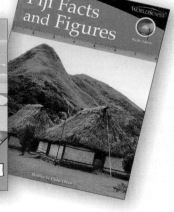

Math Library

Hands-On Materials

Manipulative Kits

- Classroom Kits
- Overhead Kits
- Student Kits
- Center Activities Kit
- Magnetic Kits (Grades K–2)

Comprehensive Digital Resources Online and on CD-ROM

eText

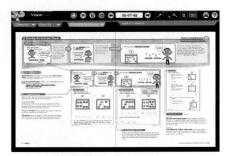

The **Teacher's Edition** allows you to plan your math lessons from home or school. Available online and on CD-ROM.

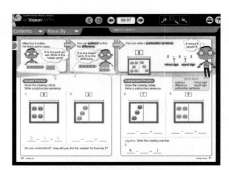

The **Student Edition** includes the complete student edition along with interactive tools and frequently used Teacher Resource Masters. Available online only.

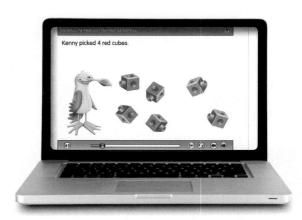

Instructional Resources

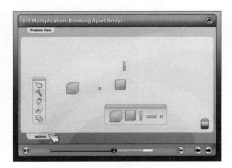

The **Tools4Math** are virtual manipulatives that let students explore and visualize concepts. Available online only.

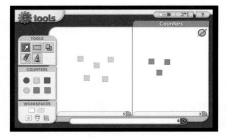

The **eTools** actively involve students with digital manipulatives that clearly demonstrate concepts. Available online only.

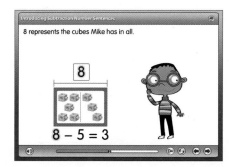

The **Visual Learning Animations** transform teaching and learning with animations that let students hear, see, and learn math concepts. Available online and on CD-ROM.

The **Animated Interactive Math Stories (K–2)** introduce new content and engage young learners with animations that bring new math concepts to life. Available online only.

The **Topic Opener Videos (3–6)** introduce new content with compelling, real-world video segments. Available online only.

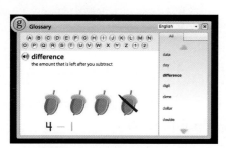

The **Animated Glossary** provides definitions and animations for new math vocabulary. Available online only.

Teacher Resources

The **Online Lesson Planner** helps you organize your lesson plans by day, week, and month. Available online.

Build a Lesson Suite assists you as you create personalized lessons in the best sequence for your students. Available online.

Examview® Assessment Suite allows you to customize tests to your state standards. Available on CD-ROM.

Professional Development

On Site Professional Development

Pearson Professional Development services help you effectively implement Common Core State Standards.

Workshops include …

- **enVisionMATH Common Core**
  An introduction to the Common Core
- **Implementing enVisionMATH Common Core**
  Compare differences from former standards

Plus these general sessions:

- **Leading the Way for Successful Common Core Implementation in Mathematics K–12**
  A general workshop on the Common Core
- **Classroom Assessment for Student Learning**
  Assessment practices for the Common Core

MyPearsonTraining.com

Online Professional Development

Learn more about the Common Core! Watch online video and tutorials 24/7 and participate in live, Web-based sessions with expert trainers.

Ask your Pearson representative for details.

Math Background

Research says that the quality of instruction depends on the teacher's knowledge of math content (Kilpatrick, 2001).

enVisionMATH Common Core provides:

- **Math Background** for teachers in every Topic Teacher's Edition
- **Math Background for Teachers** in every lesson

STEM Education

STEM or, Science, Technology, Engineering, and Mathematics, Education has as its goal increasing the number of college students choosing majoring in science or technology-related fields. STEM Education encourages a curriculum that is built around the active engagement of students in problem solving. *enVisionMATH Common Core* offers students opportunities to use mathematics to solve real-life problems in science. These opportunities are highlighted with a STEM icon that reminds students that the problem they are working on is related to science, engineering, or technology.

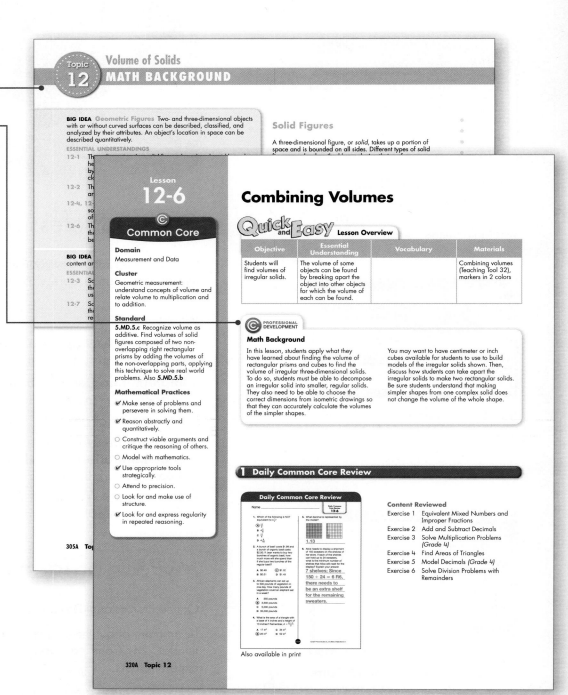

▲ **Teacher's Edition**

Development Tools

by Skip Fennell

" Together they can be valuable professional development tools, helping teachers, math leaders, and others unpack key mathematics topics within and across grade levels. "

As you begin the multi-year transition toward full implementation and assessment of the Common Core State Standards (CCSS), you will have two related opportunities for support. These are the **Progressions Documents** and the proposed products of the **Illustrative Mathematics Project.**

The **Progressions Documents** for the CCSS are a collection of narratives, generally organized around the mathematics content domains of the CCSS (e.g., Number and Operations in Base Ten). These documents trace the learning progression, across grade levels, of a particular domain or one key element of a domain. Each narrative is informed by research on learning, the logical structure of the mathematics being presented, and best practice. Together they can be valuable professional development tools, helping teachers, math leaders, and others unpack key mathematics topics within and across grade levels. The Progressions Documents, through their examination of sequence and topic emphasis within a particular domain, should help drive discussion and facilitate decisions related to the amount of time needed for particular topics, the best use of instructional tools, the influence of various mathematical practices, and other transition-related issues.

The Progressions Documents also have the potential to validate or suggest research in mathematics education. Research into the progressions can raise questions and issues that may impact the standards revision process as well as frame further research questions. Work on the Progressions Documents is supported by the Brookhill Foundation. Final documents will be available on the University of Arizona's Institute for Mathematics and Education website.

The intent of the **Illustrative Mathematics Project** is to provide guidance to states, schools, school districts, assessment consortia, testing companies, and curriculum developers by providing sample tasks to illustrate the range and type of mathematics activities that students will experience in classrooms where the CCSS are being implemented and assessed. The web-based Illustrative Mathematics Project will include a process for the submission, discussion, review, and publication of relevant learning activities or tasks. This work is being supported by the Bill and Melinda Gates Foundation; the project's site can be found through the University of Arizona's Institute for Mathematics and Education.

Meeting Individual Needs

The Common Core State Standards insist that all students must be supported in their learning so they can meet all of the standards. Differentiating instruction helps students achieve this goal.

enVisionMATH Common Core provides support for:

English Language Learners (ELL)

- **For each topic** the Meeting Individual Needs feature provides topic-specific ELL considerations plus an ELL activity.

- Each lesson's **Problem-Based Interactive Learning** activity uses instructional strategies that help all students but are especially helpful to ELL students.

- ELL strategies are also provided at the end of the lesson.

- The pictorial nature of the **Visual Learning Bridge** in each lesson also helps ELL students.

Special Needs

- **For each topic** the Meeting Individual Needs feature provides topic-specific considerations for special education students plus an activity.

- **For each lesson** the **Visual Learning Bridge** helps special education students focus on one idea at a time.

Below Level

- **For each topic** the Meeting Individual Needs feature provides topic-specific considerations for below-level students plus an activity.

- **For each lesson** the program provides an Intervention Activity, a Reteaching Master, a reference to a digital resource appropriate for below-level students, and an Intervention Lesson in the Math Diagnosis and Intervention System.

Advanced/Gifted

- **For each topic** the Meeting Individual Needs feature provides topic-specific considerations for advanced/gifted learners plus an activity.

- **For each lesson** the program provides an Advanced Center Activity, an Enrichment Master, and a reference to a digital resource appropriate for advanced students.

Topic 12 — Volume of Solids
DIFFERENTIATED INSTRUCTION

 INTERVENTION

 ELL STRATEGIES FOR ALL

Considerations for ELL Students

Hold up a reference cube when talking about a specific unit of volume. Have students frequently repeat the names of the various units and ask them to search for examples of items at home that are close to each unit of volume.

- **Beginning** Explain the terms *face*, *edge*, and *vertex* while holding up different examples of solids. Have students repeat the names as you point to them.

- **Intermediate** Students may be familiar with the use of the word *net* as a shorthand for the word *Internet*. Remind students that the term *net* is used for the plane figures that fold into solids because the interconnected lines resemble a fishing net.

- **Advanced** Students may have difficulty recognizing that the word *vertices* is the plural of the word *vertex*. Explain that it is done this way because the mathematical term comes from Latin.

Special Needs RTI

Considerations for Special-Needs Students

- For students who have difficulty drawing the representations of three-dimensional shapes, prepare worksheets that already have on them any three-dimensional shapes necessary for solving the problems.

- Plastic tracing templates are also available at art and office supply stores for drawing triangles, ellipses, parallelograms, and even three-dimensional shapes.

Below Level RTI

Considerations for Below-Level Students

- If students have a hard time finding volume using the volume formula, allow them to use cubes to model rectangular prisms. Or encourage students having difficulty to break the formula into parts by finding the area of the prism's base and then multiplying by the number of layers, which corresponds to the height.

- Encourage students to always sketch the prisms described in word problems and to label them with the dimensions given. Sketching and labeling go a long way toward avoiding errors and confusion.

Advanced/Gifted

Considerations for Advanced/Gifted Students

- Have students with strong number sense determine how many prisms with different dimensions can be made with 36 cubes. [8]

- Have students explore what happens to the volume of a rectangular prism if all of the dimensions are doubled. [The volume is multiplied by 8.] What happens if all of the dimensions are tripled? [The volume is multiplied by 27.]

Response to Intervention

RTI 1 ONGOING — Ongoing Intervention
- Lessons with guiding questions to assess understanding
- Support to prevent misconceptions and to reteach

RTI 2 STRATEGIC — Strategic Intervention
- Targeted to small groups who need more support
- Easy to implement

RTI 3 INTENSIVE — Intensive Intervention
- Instruction to accelerate progress
- Instruction focused on foundational skills

305C Topic 12

▲ **Teacher's Edition**

Reading Comprehension and Problem Solving

Research says reading comprehension plays an important role in understanding word problems in math (Mayer and Wittrock, 1996).

enVisionMATH Common Core provides:

- **Reading comprehension** strategies at the start of each topic along with questions to guide comprehension using a Problem-Solving Recording Sheet.

Vocabulary

Research says mathematics is like a language and some techniques used to learn language can be used to learn the language of math (Paris and Cunningham, 1996).

enVisionMATH Common Core provides:

- **Vocabulary Cards** in the Teacher's Resource Masters that have words on one side and definitions on the other.

- **Vocabulary Activities** in front of each topic that help students solidify their understanding of math terms.

- **Vocabulary** in lesson notes in the Teacher's Edition.

THE LANGUAGE OF MATH

MATHEMATICAL PRACTICES

Reading Comprehension and Problem Solving

Use Structure:

Using Reading Comprehension Strategies
A good reading comprehension strategy to use in math is to **determine the main idea through identifying relevant details.**

Questions to Guide Comprehension
Use these questions to guide comprehension of the problem before students give the answer to the problem.

From Lesson 12-2 Exercise 13
If 10 cubes are stacked vertically, how many cubes are not visible from the top view?

1 *What do you need to find? Circle that in the problem.* [The number of cubes not visible from the top view]

2 *What key word(s) or information is given in the problem? Underline that in the problem.* [Sample answer: The 10 cubes are stacked vertically.]

3 *What is the meaning of one of the key words given in the problem?* [Vertically means up and down.]

4 *What strategy or strategies can you use?* [Sample answer: Draw a picture.]

5 *How could you show the problem? Try drawing the stack of cubes to help you visualize the top view.* [Sample answer shown at right.]

Vocabulary Activities

Identifying Solids
Attend to Precision Give students drawings of various solids and have them count the faces, edges, and vertices of each and label an example of each term. Then, have them identify what type of solid it is.

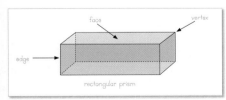

Math and Literature

Cruising the Caribbean

WorldScapes Readers™

Cruising the Caribbean For activity suggestions for pp. 4–5 of *Cruising the Caribbean*, see *Guided Problem Solving for the Math Library.*

305D

Essential Understanding

The **Essential Understanding** describes the mathematics students **will understand** related to the Common Core Standards.

All Common Core State Standards information is listed at point of use in every lesson for easy reference. Domains, Clusters, Standards, and Mathematical Practices are identified for every lesson.

Built-in **Professional Development** focuses on Mathematical Practices.

Daily Review

The **Daily Common Core Review** helps you reinforce Common Core State Standards.

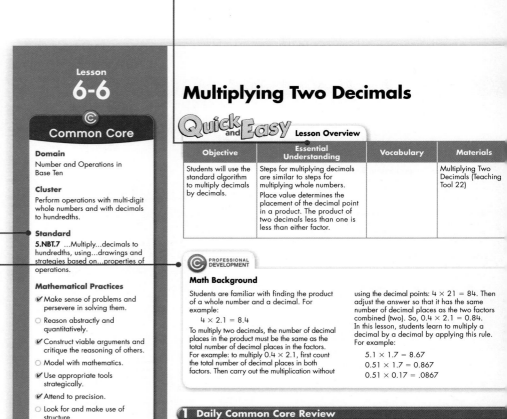

▲ **Teacher's Edition**

Problem-Based Interactive Learning

enVisionMATH Common Core provides Problem-Based Interactive Learning opportunities for effective concept development. Each Problem-Based Interactive Learning experience has four instructional phases.

- **Engage Students.**

  Set the Purpose of the activity. Then ask and discuss the Connect question to help students recall prior knowledge.

- **Students Solve and Discuss a Problem.**

  Pose the Problem. Have students work together to solve the problems as the teacher facilitates (observes, asks questions, etc.).

  Have students share their thinking and work. When possible, show more than one solution.

- **Make the Important Math Explicit.**

  For a classroom conversation use the questions and ideas that follow **Pose the Problem.**

- **Deepen Understanding.**

  Extend. As time permits, provide the problem extension to increase knowledge and depth of understanding.

Observe **Mathematical Practices** during Problem-Based Interactive Learning.

---

2 Develop the Concept: Interactive

 MATHEMATICAL PRACTICES

 10–15 min **Problem-Based Interactive Learning**

Overview Students explore the product of two decimals by linking it to the product of a whole number and a decimal.

Focus How can you multiply two decimals?

Materials Teaching Tool 22

 Set the Purpose *You know how to multiply a whole number and a decimal. Today you will learn to multiply two decimals.*

Connect *When in everyday life do you multiply with decimals?* [Possible response: finding the cost of two identical items]

Pose the Problem Distribute a copy of Teaching Tool 22 to each student. *Suppose you are going to make fruit salad and need the amounts shown. About how much will each kind of fruit cost? Record your answers in the first empty column.* Provide time to work. Have students share how they found their estimates.

Link to Prior Knowledge *Why did you not find exact costs?* [The question asked *about* how much.] *How do you estimate?* [Round factors to the nearest whole numbers.] *How did you multiply a whole number and a decimal?* [Multiply as whole numbers. Count decimal places in the factors and insert the decimal in the product the same number of places from the right.]

Instruct in Small Steps *To find the exact costs, multiply the decimals as if they were whole numbers. This gives the correct digits of the product. Record each product in the next column.* Allow time to multiply. *Compare your estimates with the exact costs. Place the decimal point so both answers are as close as possible.* Allow time to place the decimals. *What patterns do you notice?* [The total number of decimal places in the factors is the same as that in the product.] *How can you make the costs practical?* [Round to the nearest penny.] *Record in the last column.* Give students time to complete the last column.

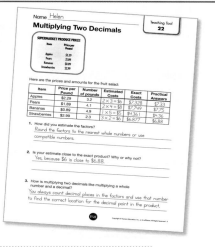

 Suppose you are finding 0.425 × 0.565. Without finding the exact answer, do you think the product will be greater or less than 1? Explain. [The product will be less than 1 since you are finding a fractional part of an amount less than 1.]

158B

Visual Learning

Step-by-step **Visual Instruction** makes the math explicit for students and parents.

- **Visual concept development** that helps students access math skills and concepts by seeing ideas developed in visual displays.

- **Visual Learning Bridge** which is a pictorial, step-by-step bridge between the Problem-Based Interactive Learning activity and the lesson exercises. It helps students focus on one idea at a time as well as see connections within a sequence of ideas. This is especially helpful for visual learners and English language learners.

- **Guiding questions** in blue type that help you guide students through the examples and give you an opportunity to check students' understanding.

- **Pictures with a purpose** throughout the lessons that show representations of math concepts and show data for math problems in real-world contexts.

MATHEMATICAL PRACTICES

During **Guided Practice**, students are explaining, writing, and creating their own problems.

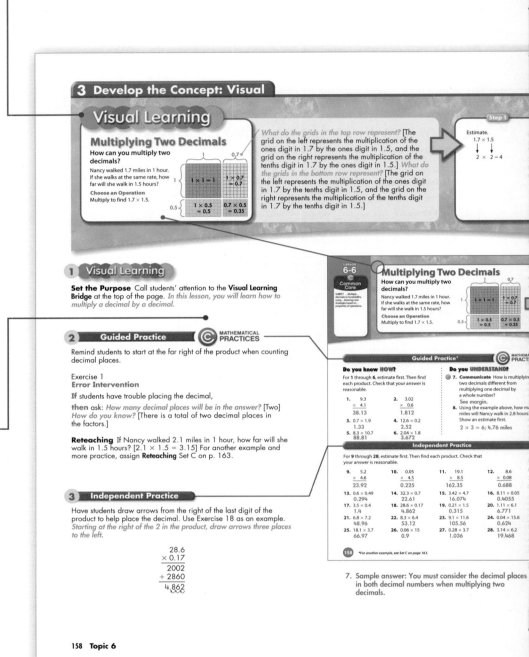

▲ **Teacher's Edition**

Visual Learning Animations

Visual Learning Animations can be used to present the Visual Learning Bridge digitally with animation. The content of each student lesson comes alive in the Visual Learning Animations. These animations provide additional questions and promote deeper understanding of concepts.

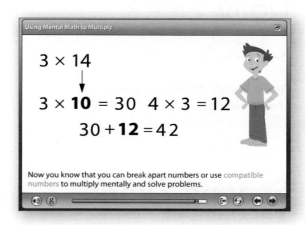

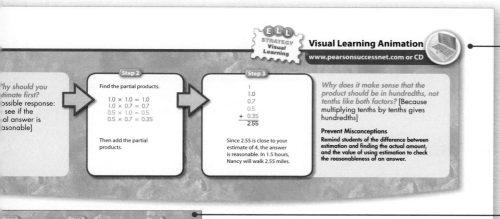

Visual Learning Animation
www.pearsonsuccessnet.com or CD

Step 2
Find the partial products.

$1.0 \times 1.0 = 1.0$
$1.0 \times 0.7 = 0.7$
$0.5 \times 1.0 = 0.5$
$0.5 \times 0.7 = 0.35$

Then add the partial products.

Step 3

$\begin{array}{r} 1.0 \\ 0.7 \\ 0.5 \\ + \ 0.35 \\ \hline 2.55 \end{array}$

Since 2.55 is close to your estimate of 4, the answer is reasonable. In 1.5 hours, Nancy will walk 2.55 miles.

Why does it make sense that the product should be in hundredths, not tenths like both factors? [Because multiplying tenths by tenths gives hundredths]

Prevent Misconceptions
Remind students of the difference between estimation and finding the actual amount, and the value of using estimation to check the reasonableness of an answer.

Problem Solving  MATHEMATICAL PRACTICES

Students use underlying processes and mathematical tools for Exercises 29–35. Remind students to check for reasonableness when solving each problem.

Exercise 32
Attend to Precision Make sure students recognize this as a multiplication situation. Creative students may realize that you can double 16.5, and then double the resulting product to get the answer. Ask *If you double a number, and then double it again, by what factor are you multiplying?* [a factor of 4]

Exercise 33
Construct Arguments Remind students that they may need to obtain information that is not given explicitly in the problem. *To find how much Mary Ann spent, what is the hidden question you need to find first?* [The total cost of 3 pens.]

Early Finishers *Look at Exercise 34. Suppose that the space suit weighed 7.93 times as much on Earth. About how much would the suit weigh on Earth?* [About 240 pounds]

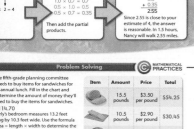

Step 2
Find the partial products.

$1.0 \times 1.0 = 1.0$
$1.0 \times 0.7 = 0.7$
$0.5 \times 1.0 = 0.5$
$0.5 \times 0.7 = 0.35$

Then add the partial products.

Step 3

$\begin{array}{r} 1.0 \\ 0.7 \\ 0.5 \\ + \ 0.35 \\ \hline 2.55 \end{array}$

Since 2.55 is close to your estimate of 4, the answer is reasonable. In 1.5 hours, Nancy will walk 2.55 miles.

Problem Solving MATHEMATICAL PRACTICES

the fifth-grade planning committee needs to buy items for sandwiches for its annual lunch. Fill in the chart and determine the amount of money they'll need to buy the items for sandwiches.

Item	Amount	Price	Total
	15.5 pounds	$3.50 per pound	$54.25
	10.5 pounds	$2.90 per pound	$30.45
	12 packages	$2.50 per package	$30.00

...114.70

...arly's bedroom measures 13.2 feet ...ng by 10.3 feet wide. Use the formula ...ea = length × width to determine the ...mber of square feet for the floor of ...arly's bedroom.
...35.96 ft²

...bag of grass seed weighs 5.8 pounds. ...ow many pounds would 2.5 bags weigh?
...14.5
13.8
8.3
3.3

32. Be Precise Joy drinks 4 bottles of water per day. Each bottle contains 16.5 fluid ounces. How many fluid ounces of water does she drink per day?

(A) 66 fluid ounces   C 660 fluid ounces
B 68 fluid ounces   D 680 fluid ounces

...onstruct Arguments Mary Ann ...dered 3 pens and a box of paper on ...e Internet. Each pen cost $1.65 and ...e paper cost $3.95 per box. How ...uch did she spend?
...8.90

...riting to Explain How does ...timation help you place the decimal ...int in a product correctly?
...ee margin.

34. An astronaut's Apollo space suit weighs 29.8 pounds on the moon. It weighs approximately 6.02 times as much on Earth. About how much does an Apollo space suit weigh on Earth?
About 180 pounds

Lesson 6-5 (159)

...5. Sample answer: If the decimal point is misplaced in the actual product, the product won't be close to the estimate.

159

Visual Learning Bridge

A **Visual Learning Bridge** is shown at the start of the lesson in the Student Edition and also appears in the Teacher's Edition along with guiding questions in blue type.

MATHEMATICAL PRACTICES

Problem-solving exercises apply Mathematical Practices and higher-order thinking.

Assessment and Prescription

Assess understanding, differentiate instruction, and observe the 8 Mathematical Practices in action with teacher-guided and independent-leveled Center Activities.

Daily Quick Check

Daily Quick Check assesses student understanding with an eye toward differentiation for individual student needs.

Scoring Rubric

Scoring Rubric includes three levels of performance and samples of student work.

Prescription

Prescription is provided for Differentiated Instruction.

---

4 Close/Assess and Differentiate

Close
Essential Understanding Steps for multiplying decimals are similar to steps for multiplying whole numbers. Place value determines the placement of the decimal point in a product. The product of two decimals less than one is less than either factor. *In this lesson, you learned how to use place value to determine the placement of the decimal when multiplying decimals by decimals.*

ASSESSMENT

Exercises 1–4 are worth 1 point each.
Use the rubric to score Exercise 5.

Exercise 5
Writing to Explain Students should be able to multiply two decimal numbers together and show their answer with the correct number of decimal places.

ELL Model Thinking Aloud Help children to verbalize what they are thinking. Say: *I notice that there are 2 decimal places in each factor so the product will have . . .*

Student Samples
3-point answer The student estimates the answer by multiplying 2 × 8. The multiplication shows the process of calculation and obtains the correct value: 17.1936.

> The estimated value is 2 × 8 = 16
> 7.96
> × 2.16
> 4776
> 7960
> +159200
> 17.1936

2-point answer The student accurately estimates the answer and calculates the product but does not show work.

> The estimated value is 16.
> The calculated value is
> 17.1936

1-point answer The student accurately estimates the value but places the decimal point incorrectly in the calculated answer.

> The estimated value is 2 × 8 = 16
> 7.96
> × 2.16
> 4776
> 7960
> + 49200
> 1719.36

Quick Check Master

Name _____ Quick Check 6-6

1. How many decimal places will there be in the product shown below?
23.58 × 14.2 = ?
   A. one
   B. two
   C. three
   D. four

2. Find the product: 24.66 × 12.3.
   A. 30.2066
   B. 302.088
   C. 3,020.88
   D. 302,088

3. The cost of a piece of fabric is $1.32 per yard. How much does a 3.5-yard piece of fabric cost?
   A. $1.62
   B. $3.76
   C. $3.84
   D. $4.62

4. Your classroom is 11.4 meters long and 8.4 meters wide. What is the floor area of the classroom in square meters? Use the formula area = length × width.
   A. 957.60 m²
   B. 195.34 m²
   C. 95.76 m²
   D. 92.88 m²

5. **Writing to Explain** Estimate the product of the numbers 2.16 and 7.96. Then multiply to find the exact answer. Show your work.
   See student samples at the right.

Formative Assessment

Use the **Quick Check** to assess students' understanding.

Prescription for Differentiated Instruction
Use student work on the **Quick Check** to prescribe differentiated instruction.

Points	Prescription
0–5	Intervention
6	On-Level
7	Advanced

159A Topic 6

▲ Teacher's Edition

Data-Driven Differentiated Instruction

Assign your students the appropriate level of Intervention, Practice or Enrichment.

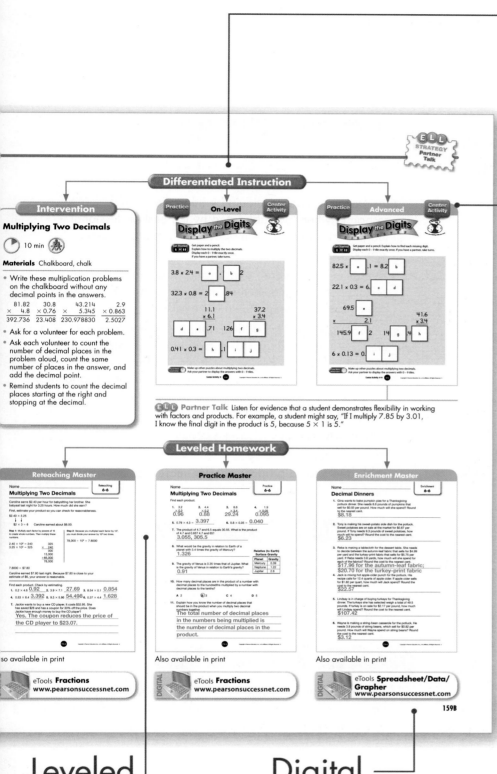

ELL Partner Talk Listen for evidence that a student demonstrates flexibility in working with factors and products. For example, a student might say, "If I multiply 7.85 by 3.01, I know the final digit in the product is 5, because 5 × 1 is 5."

Leveled Homework

Leveled Homework promotes proficiency before End-of-Topic assessments.

Digital Resources

Digital Resources Include eTools, Games, and MindPoint Quiz Show.

Center Activities

- **Ready-made** practice for every lesson.
- **Multiple uses**
  - Extend the activity by using the "If You Have More Time" feature
  - Ongoing review
  - Reuse year after year
- **ELL Strong ELL Strategies** encourage students to share their thinking.
- **Easy-to-manage, independent work** There are seven repeating activity formats.

The Center Activity formats are:

- **Clip and Cover** Students use number cubes and paper clips to select information. Students answer questions, cover answers in game spaces on a gameboard, and win when four spaces in a row are covered.
- **Display the Digits** Students answer questions, explain their thinking, and use number tiles to display their answers.
- **Quick Questions** Students toss number cubes, answer questions that have answers from 1 to 6.
- **Teamwork** Students each pick a number to determine which student will explain that numbered step in a multi-step process.
- **Think Together** Students are given a question and four answer choices. They each pick a number to determine who will discuss each answer choice.
- **Tic Tac Toe** Students toss number cubes, use an algebraic rule to compute with the numbers, and cover answers in game spaces on gameboards.
- **Toss and Talk** Students toss number cubes, explain how to answer a question next to the sum of the numbers, and win by getting connected rectangles on a four-by-four gameboard.

Findings and Recommendations

The **National Mathematics Advisory Panel's Final Report** included the following findings and recommendations on topics that included instructional practices, materials, professional development, and assessments.

Core Principles of Math Instruction

- The areas to be studied in mathematics from pre-kindergarten through eighth grade should be streamlined and a well-defined set of the most important topics should be emphasized in the early grades. Any approach that revisits topics year after year without bringing them to closure should be avoided.

- Proficiency with whole numbers, fractions, and certain aspects of geometry and measurement are the foundations for algebra. Of these, knowledge of fractions is the most important foundational skill....

- Conceptual understanding, computational and procedural fluency, and problem-solving skills are equally important and mutually reinforce each other....

- Students should develop immediate recall of arithmetic facts to free the "working memory" for solving more complex problems.

- The benchmarks set forth by the Panel should help to guide classroom curricula, mathematics instruction, textbook development, and state assessments.

- More students should be prepared for and offered an authentic algebra course at Grade 8.

- Algebra should be consistently understood in terms of the "Major Topics of School Algebra," as defined by the National Math Panel.

- The Major Topics of School Algebra include symbols and expressions; linear equations; quadratic equations; functions; algebra of polynomials; and combinatorics and finite probability.

Effective Instruction Matters

- Teachers' regular use of formative assessments can improve student learning in mathematics.

- Instructional practice should be informed by high-quality research, when available, and by the best professional judgment and experience of accomplished classroom teachers.

- The belief that children of particular ages cannot learn certain content because they are "too young" or "not ready" has consistently been shown to be false.

- Explicit instruction for students who struggle with math is effective in increasing student learning. Teachers should understand how to provide clear models for solving a problem type using an array of examples, offer opportunities for extensive practice, encourage students to "think aloud," and give specific feedback.

- Mathematically gifted students should be allowed to accelerate their learning.

- Publishers should produce shorter, more focused and mathematically accurate mathematics textbooks....

Effective Assessment

- The National Assessment of Educational Progress (NAEP) and state assessments in mathematics should be improved in quality and should emphasize the most critical knowledge and skills leading to Algebra.

Importance of Research

- The nation must continue to build the capacity for more rigorous research in mathematics education to inform policy and practice more effectively.

NCTM Curriculum Focal Points and Connections

NCTM Curriculum Focal Points and Connections for Grade 5
The set of three curriculum focal points and related connections for mathematics in Grade 5 follow. These topics are the recommended content emphases for this grade level. It is essential that these focal points be addressed in contexts that promote problem solving, reasoning, communication, making connections, and designing and analyzing representations.

Grade 5 Curriculum Focal Points

Number and Operations and Algebra: Developing an understanding of and fluency with division of whole numbers

Students apply their understanding of models for division, place value, properties, and the relationship of division to multiplication as they develop, discuss, and use efficient, accurate, and generalizable procedures to find quotients involving multidigit dividends. They select appropriate methods and apply them accurately to estimate quotients or calculate them mentally, depending on the context and numbers involved. They develop fluency with efficient procedures, including the standard algorithm, for dividing whole numbers, understand why the procedures work (on the basis of place value and properties of operations), and use them to solve problems. They consider the context in which a problem is situated to select the most useful form of the quotient for the solution, and they interpret it appropriately.

Number and Operations: Developing an understanding of and fluency with addition and subtraction of fractions and decimals

Students apply their understandings of fractions and fraction models to represent the addition and subtraction of fractions with unlike denominators as equivalent calculations with like denominators. They apply their understandings of decimal models, place value, and properties to add and subtract decimals. They develop fluency with standard procedures for adding and subtracting fractions and decimals. They make reasonable estimates of fraction and decimal sums and differences. Students add and subtract fractions and decimals to solve problems, including problems involving measurement.

Geometry and Measurement and Algebra: Describing three-dimensional shapes and analyzing their properties, including volume and surface area

Students relate two-dimensional shapes to three-dimensional shapes and analyze properties of polyhedral solids, describing them by the number of edges, faces, or vertices as well as the types of faces. Students recognize volume as an attribute of three-dimensional space. They understand that they can quantify volume by finding the total number of same-sized units of volume that they need to fill the space without gaps or overlaps. They understand that a cube that is 1 unit on an edge is the standard unit for measuring volume. They select appropriate units, strategies, and tools for solving problems that involve estimating or measuring volume. They decompose three-dimensional shapes and find surface areas and volumes of prisms. As they work with surface area, they find and justify relationships among the formulas for the areas of different polygons. They measure necessary attributes of shapes to use area formulas to solve problems.

Connections to the Focal Points

Algebra: Students use patterns, models, and relationships as contexts for writing and solving simple equations and inequalities. They create graphs of simple equations. They explore prime and composite numbers and discover concepts related to the addition and subtraction of fractions as they use factors and multiples, including applications of common factors and common multiples. They develop an understanding of the order of operations and use it for all operations.

Measurement: Students' experiences connect their work with solids and volume to their earlier work with capacity and weight or mass. They solve problems that require attention to both approximation and precision of measurement.

Data Analysis: Students apply their understanding of whole numbers, fractions, and decimals as they construct and analyze double-bar and line graphs and use ordered pairs on coordinate grids.

Number and Operations: Building on their work in Grade 4, students extend their understanding of place value to numbers through millions and millionths in various contexts. They apply what they know about multiplication of whole numbers to larger numbers. Students also explore contexts that they can describe with negative numbers (e.g., situations of owing money or measuring elevations above and below sea level).

Research Bibliography

Research Referenced in the Teacher's Editions

Baroody, A. J. *Children's Mathematical Thinking.* New York: Teacher's College, Columbia University, 1987.

Behr, M. J., Harel, G., Post, T., and Lesh, R. "Rational Number, Ratio, and Proportion." In D. A. Grouws (Ed.), *Handbook of Research on Mathematics Teaching and Learning* (1992), pp. 296–333.

Behr, M. J., I. Wachsmuth, T. R. Post, and R. Lesh. "Order and Equivalence of Rational Numbers: A Clinical Teaching Experiment." *Journal for Research in Mathematics Education,* 15 (1984), pp. 323–341.

Bell, A.W. "Diagnosing Students' Misconceptions." *The Australian Mathematics Teacher* 1 (1982): 6–10.

Black, P. and William, D. "Assessment and Classroom Learning." In *Assessment and Education.* Special Issue of Assessment in Education: Principles, Policy, and Practice. 5 (1) (1998): 7–75.

Booth, L. R. "Children's Difficulties in Beginning Algebra." In *The Ideas of Algebra, K–12.* Edited by A. F. Coxford, pp. 20–32. Reston, VA: National Council of Teachers of Mathematics, 1988.

Bright, G. W., and K. Hoeffner. "Measurement, Probability, Statistics, and Graphing." In *Research Ideas for the Classroom: Middle Grades Mathematics.* Edited by D. T. Owens, pp. 78–98. Reston, VA: National Council of Teachers of Mathematics, 1993.

Burns, M. "About Teaching Mathematics: A K–8 Resource." Sausalito, CA: Math Solutions Publications, 2000.

Carpenter, T., and E. Fennema. "Cognitively Guided Instruction: Building on the Knowledge of Students and Teachers." *International Journal of Educational Research.* Special Issue: The Case of Mathematics in the United States. W. Secada (Ed.), (1992), pp. 457–470.

Charles, R. *Math Across the Grades.* Boston: Pearson, 2005.

Cognition and Technology Group at Vanderbilt. "Looking at Technology in Context: A Framework for Understanding Technology and Education Research." *The Handbook of Educational Psychology,* D. C. Berliner and R. C. Calfee, eds. NY: Macmillan. (1996), pp. 807–840.

Cotton, K. "Monitoring Student Learning in the Classroom." Portland, OR, Northwest Regional Educational Laboratory. (2001).

Cuevas, G. J., P. H. Mann, and R. M. McClung. "The Effects of a Language Process Approach Program on the Mathematics Achievements of First, Third, and Fifth Graders." Paper presented at the meeting of the American Educational Research Association, San Francisco, CA (1986).

Dick, W., and L. Carey. *The Systematic Design of Instruction* (4th ed.). New York: Harper Collins College Publishers, 1996.

Diezmann and English. "The Roles of Representation in School Mathematics." Virginia: NCTM. (2003), p. 88.

Dreher, M. J. "Fostering Reading for Learning." In L. Baker, M. J. Dreher, and J.T. Guthrie (Eds.), *Engaging Young Readers: Promoting Achievement and Motivation* (2000), pp. 68–93.

Empson, Susan B. "Low-Performing Students and Teaching Fractions for Understanding: An Interactional Analysis." *Journal for Research in Mathematics Education* 34 (4) (2003), pp. 305–343.

Gagné, R. M. *The Conditions of Learning* (4th ed.). New York: Holt, Rinehart and Winston, Inc., 1977.

Graeber, A. O., and E. Tanenhaus. "Multiplication and Division: From Whole Numbers to Rational Numbers." In *Research Ideas for the Classroom: Middle Grades Mathematics.* Edited by D. T. Owens, pp. 99–117. Reston, VA: National Council of Teachers of Mathematics, 1993.

Hiebert, J. *Conceptual and Procedural Knowledge: The Case of Mathematics.* Hillsdale, NJ: Erlbaum, 1986.

Hiebert, J., and M. J. Behr. "Capturing the Major Themes." In *Number Concepts and Operations in the Middle Grades.* Edited by J. Hiebert and M. J. Behr, pp. 1–18. Hillsdale, NJ: Erlbaum; Reston, VA: National Council of Teachers of Mathematics, 1988.

Hiebert, J., T. P. Carpenter, E. Fennema, K.C. Fuson, D. Wearne, H. Murray, A. Olivier, and P. Human. *Making Sense: Teaching and Learning Mathematics With Understanding.* Portsmouth, NH: Heinemann, 1997.

Hong, H. "Effects of Mathematics Learning through Children's Literature on Math Achievement and Dispositional Outcomes." *Early Childhood Research Quarterly* 11 (4) (1996), pp. 477–494.

Kenney, P. A., and E. A. Silver, eds. "Results from the Sixth Mathematics Assessment of the National Assessment of Educational Progress." Reston, VA: National Council of Teachers of Mathematics, 1997.

Kilpatrick, Jeremy. *A Research Companion to Principles and Standards for School Mathematics.* Reston, VA: National Council of Teachers of Mathematics, 2003.

Kouba, V.L., C. Brown, T. Carpenter, M. Lindquist, E. Silver, and J. Swafford. "Results of the Fourth NAEP Assessment of Mathematics: Number, Operations, and Word Problems." *Arithmetic Teacher,* 35 (1988), pp. 14–19.

Kouba, V. L., and K. Franklin. "Multiplication and Division: Sense Making and Meaning." In *Research Ideas for the Classroom: Early Childhood Mathematics.* Edited by R. Jensen. New York: Macmillan Publishing Company, 1993.

Lodholz, R. D. "The Transition from Arithmetic to Algebra." In *Algebra For Everyone.* Edited by E.L. Edwards, Jr., pp. 24–33. Reston, VA: National Council of Teachers of Mathematics, 1990.

Mack, N. K. "Learning Fractions with Understanding: Building on Informal Knowledge." *Journal for Research in Mathematics Education* 21 (1990), pp. 16–32.

Martin, G. and Strutchens, M. E. (2000). "Geometry and Measurement" in E. A. Silver and P. A. Kenney (Eds.) *Results from the Seventh Mathematics Assessment of the National Assessment of Educational Progress* (pp. 193–234). Reston, VA: National Council of Teachers of Mathematics.

Mathematics Learning Study Committee. *Adding It Up: Helping Children Learn Mathematics.* Edited by J. Kilpatrick, J. Swafford, and B. Findell. Washington, D.C.: National Academy Press, 2001.

Mayer, R. E. "Models for Understanding." *Review of Research in Education,* 59 (1989), pp. 43–64.

Mayer, R. E., and M. C. Wittrock. "Problem-Solving Transfer." In D. C. Berliner and R. C. Calfee (Eds.), *Handbook of Educational Psychology* (1996), pp. 47–62.

National Council of Teachers of Mathematics. *Principles and Standards for School Mathematics.* Reston, VA: National Council of Teachers of Mathematics, 2000.

National Mathematics Advisory Panel. *The Final Report of the National Mathematics Advisory Panel.* Washington, DC: U. S. Department of Education, 2008.

Nesher, P. "Multiplicative School Word Problems: Theoretical approaches and empirical findings." In J. Hiebert and M. Behr (Eds.) *Number Concepts and Operations in the Middle Grades.* Reston, VA: NCTM (1988), pp. 162–181.

Payne, J. N., A. E. Towsley, and D. M. Huinker. "Fractions and Decimals" In Mathematics for the Young Child. Edited by J. Payne, pp. 175–200. Reston, VA: National Council of Teachers of Mathematics.

Pesek, Dolores D., and David Kirshner. "Interference of Instrumental Instruction in Subsequent Relational Learning." *Journal for Research in Mathematics Education* 31 (5) (2000), pp. 524–540.

Pike, C. L. "The Use of Symbols, Words, and Diagrams as Indicators of Mathematical Cognition: A causal model." *Journal for Research in Mathematics Education,* 34 (2003), pp. 406–432.

Reys, B. J., and R. E. Reys. "Estimation-Directions from the Standards." *Arithmetic Teacher,* 37 (7) (1990), pp. 22–25.

Richards, D. D., and R. S. Siegler. "The Development of Time, Speed, and Distance Concepts." Paper presented at the Biennial Meeting of the Society for Research in Child Development (San Francisco, California, March 15–18, 1979).

Rittle-Johnson, B., and R. S. Siegler. "The Relation Between Conceptual and Procedural Knowledge in Learning Mathematics: A Review." In *The Development of Mathematical Skills.* Edited by C. Donlon, pp. 75–110. East Sussex, UK: Psychology Press, 1998.

Schwartz, D. L. and Heiser, J. "Spatial Representations and Imagery in Learning." In R. K. Sawyer (Ed.), *The Cambridge Handbook of the Learning Sciences* (2006), pp. 283–298.

Van de Walle, J. *Elementary and Middle School Mathematics.* Boston: Pearson, 2004.

Vye, N. J., D. L. Schwartz, J. D. Bransford, B. J. Barron, L. Zech, and Cognition and Technology Group at Vanderbilt. "SMART Environments That Support Monitoring, Reflection, and Revision." *Metacognition in Educational Theory and Practice.* D. Hacker, J. Dunlosky, and A. Graessner, eds. Mahwah, NJ: Erlbaum (1998).

Wearne, D., J. Hiebert, and S. Taber. "Fourth Graders' Gradual Construction of Decimal Fractions During Instruction Using Different Physical Representations." *Elementary School Journal,* 91 (4) (1991), pp. 321–341.

Wilson, P., and A. Osborne. "Foundational Ideas in Teaching About Measurement." In *Teaching Mathematics in Grades K–8: Research Based Methods.* Edited by T. Post. Boston: Allyn and Bacon, 1988.

MathStart® Bibliography

Books in the MathStart® Series

Animals on Board (Adding)

Beep, Beep, Vroom Vroom! (Pattern Recognition)

The Best Bug Parade (Comparing Sizes)

The Best Vacation Ever (Collecting Data)

Betcha! (Estimating)

Bigger, Better, Best! (Area)

Bug Dance (Directions)

Captain Invincible and the Space Shapes (Three-Dimensional Shapes)

Circus Shapes (Recognizing Shapes)

Coyotes All Around (Rounding)

Dave's Down to Earth Rock Shop (Classifying)

Dinosaur Deals (Equivalent Values)

Divide and Ride (Dividing)

Double the Ducks (Doubling Numbers)

Earth Day Hooray! (Place Value)

Elevator Magic (Subtracting)

Every Buddy Counts (Counting)

A Fair Bear Share (Regrouping)

Game Time! (Time)

Get Up and Go! (Timelines)

Give Me Half! (Understanding Halves)

The Greatest Gymnast of All (Opposites)

The Grizzly Gazette (Percentage)

Hamster Champs (Angles)

Henry the Fourth (Ordinals)

A House for Birdie (Understanding Capacity)

It's About Time (Hours)

Jack the Builder (Counting On)

Jump, Kangaroo, Jump! (Fractions)

Just Enough Carrots (Comparing Amounts)

Leaping Lizards (Counting by 5s and 10s)

Lemonade for Sale (Bar Graphs)

Less than Zero (Negative Numbers)

Let's Fly a Kite (Symmetry)

Mall Mania (Addition Strategies)

Mighty Maddie (Odd and Even Numbers)

Missing Mittens (Odd and Even Numbers)

Monster Musical Chairs (Subtracting One)

More or Less (Comparing Numbers)

One... Two... Three... Sassafras! (Number Order)

100 Days of Cool (Numbers 1–100)

A Pair of Socks (Matching)

The Penny Pot (Counting Coins)

Pepper's Journal (Calendars)

Polly's Pen Pal (Metrics)

Probably Pistachio (Probability)

Rabbit's Pajama Party (Sequencing)

Racing Around (Perimeter)

Ready, Set, Hop! (Building Equations)

Rodeo Time (Reading a Schedule)

Room for Ripley (Capacity)

Safari Park (Solving for Unknowns)

Same Old Horse (Making Predictions)

Seaweed Soup (Matching Sets)

Shark Swimathon (Subtracting 2-Digit Numbers)

Sluggers' Car Wash (Dollars and Cents)

The Sundae Scoop (Combinations)

Super Sand Castle Saturday (Measuring)

Spunky Monkeys on Parade (Counting by 2s, 3s, and 4s)

Tally O'Malley (Tallying)

3 Little Firefighters (Sorting)

Too Many Kangaroo Things to Do! (Multiplication)

Treasure Map (Mapping)

Glossary

acute angle An angle whose measure is between 0° and 90°.

acute triangle A triangle whose angles are all acute angles.

Addition Property of Equality The same number can be added to both sides of an equation and the sides remain equal.

algebraic expression A mathematical phrase involving a variable or variables, numbers, and operations.
Example: $x - 3$

angle Two rays that have the same endpoint.

area The number of square units needed to cover a surface or figure.

Associative Property of Addition Addends can be regrouped and the sum remains the same.
Example: $1 + (3 + 5) = (1 + 3) + 5$

Associative Property of Multiplication Factors can be regrouped and the product remains the same.
Example: $2 \times (4 \times 10) = (2 \times 4) \times 10$

axis (plural: axes) Either of two lines drawn perpendicular to each other in a graph.

base (in arithmetic) The number that is multiplied by itself when raised to a power.
Example: In 5^3, the 5 is the base.

base (of a polygon) The side of a polygon to which the height is perpendicular.

base (of a solid) The face of a solid that is used to name the solid.

Base

benchmark fraction Common fractions used for estimating, such as $\frac{1}{4}$, $\frac{1}{3}$, $\frac{1}{2}$, $\frac{2}{3}$, and $\frac{3}{4}$.

capacity The volume of a container measured in liquid units.

Celsius (°C) A unit of measure for measuring temperature in the metric system.

center The point from which all points in a circle are equally distant.

centimeter (cm) A metric unit of length. 100 centimeters equal 1 meter.

432

circle A closed plane figure made up of all the points that are the same distance from a given point.

common denominator A number that is the denominator of two or more fractions.

common multiple A number that is a multiple of two or more numbers.

Commutative Property of Addition
The order of addends can be changed and the sum remains the same.
Example: 3 + 7 = 7 + 3

Commutative Property of Multiplication
The order of factors can be changed and the product remains the same.
Example: 3 × 5 = 5 × 3

compatible numbers Numbers that are easy to compute with mentally.

compensation Adjusting one number of an operation to make computations easier and balancing the adjustment by changing the other number.

composite number A whole number greater than 1 with more than 2 factors.

cone A solid figure with one circular base; the points on the circle are joined to one point outside the base.

congruent figures Figures that have the same size and shape.

coordinate grid A grid that makes it easy to locate points in a plane using an ordered pair of numbers.

coordinates The two numbers in an ordered pair.

corresponding Matching terms in a pattern.

cube A solid figure with six flat surfaces called faces. All the faces are squares.

cubed A name for a number to the third power.

cubic unit The volume of a cube that measures 1 unit on each edge.

cup (c) A customary unit of capacity. 1 cup equals 8 fluid ounces.

cylinder A solid figure with two circular bases that are congruent and parallel.

data Collected information.

decimal A number with one or more places to the right of a decimal point.

433

degree (°) A unit of measure for angles.

denominator The number below the fraction bar in a fraction.

difference The number that results from subtracting one number from another.

digits The symbols used to show numbers: 0, 1, 2, 3, 4, 5, 6, 7, 8, 9.

Distributive Property Multiplying a sum (or difference) by a number is the same as multiplying each number in the sum (or difference) by the number and adding (or subtracting) the products. *Example:* $3 \times (10 + 4) = (3 \times 10) + (3 \times 4)$

dividend The number to be divided.

divisible A number is divisible by another number if there is no remainder after dividing.

Division Property of Equality Both sides of an equation can be divided by the same nonzero number and the sides remain equal.

divisor The number used to divide another number.

edge A line segment where two faces meet in a solid figure.

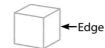

←Edge

elapsed time The difference between two times.

equation A number sentence that uses an equal sign to show that two expressions have the same value. *Example:* $9 + 3 = 12$

equilateral triangle A triangle whose sides all have the same length.

equivalent decimals Decimals that name the same amount. *Example:* $0.7 = 0.70$

equivalent fractions Fractions that name the same part of a whole region, length, or set.

estimate To give an approximate value rather than an exact answer.

evaluate To find the value of an expression.

expanded form A way to write a number that shows the place value of each digit. *Example:* $3{,}000 + 500 + 60 + 2$

expanded form (exponents) A way to write a number involving exponents that shows the base as a factor.

exponent A number that tells how many times the base is used as a factor. *Example:* $10^3 = 10 \times 10 \times 10$; the exponent is 3 and the base is 10.

exponential notation A way to write a number using a base and an exponent.

face A flat surface of a polyhedron.

←Face

434

factors Numbers that are multiplied to get a product.

Fahrenheit (°F) A unit of measure for measuring temperature in the customary system.

fluid ounce (fl oz) A customary unit of capacity equal to 2 tablespoons.

formula A rule that uses symbols.

fraction A symbol, such as $\frac{2}{3}$, $\frac{5}{1}$, or $\frac{8}{5}$, used to describe one or more parts of a whole that is divided into equal parts. A fraction can name a part of a whole, a part of a set, a location on a number line, or a division of whole numbers.

frequency table A table used to show the number of times something occurs.

gallon (gal) A unit for measuring capacity in the customary system. 1 gallon equals 4 quarts.

generalization A general statement. *Example:* A generalization about rectangles applies to all rectangles.

gram (g) A metric unit of mass. One gram is equal to 1,000 milligrams.

height of a polygon The length of a segment from one vertex of a polygon perpendicular to its base.

height of a solid In a prism or cylinder, the perpendicular distance between the bases of the figure. In a cone or pyramid, the measure of a line segment from the vertex of the figure perpendicular to the base of the figure.

hexagon A polygon with 6 sides.

hundredth One part of 100 equal parts of a whole.

Identity Property of Multiplication The property that states that the product of any number and 1 is that number.

improper fraction A fraction whose numerator is greater than or equal to its denominator.

intersecting lines Lines that pass through the same point.

interval (on a graph) The difference between adjoining numbers on an axis of a graph.

inverse operations Operations that undo each other. *Example:* Adding 6 and subtracting 6 are inverse operations.

isosceles triangle A triangle with two sides of the same length.

435

kilogram (kg) A metric unit of mass. One kilogram is equal to 1,000 grams.

kilometer (km) A metric unit of length. One kilometer is equal to 1,000 meters.

least common denominator (LCD) The least common multiple of the denominators of two or more fractions.

least common multiple (LCM) The least number that is a common multiple of two or more numbers.

line A straight path of points that goes on forever in two directions.

line graph A graph that connects points to show how data change over time.

line of symmetry The fold line in a symmetric figure.

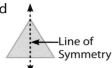
Line of Symmetry

line plot A display of responses along a number line with Xs recorded above the responses to indicate the number of times a response occurred.

line segment Part of a line having two endpoints.

line symmetry A figure has line symmetry when it can be folded along one or more lines that create congruent parts, which can fit on top of each other exactly.

liter (L) A metric unit of capacity. One liter is equal to 1,000 milliliters.

mass The measure of the quantity of matter in an object.

meter (m) A metric unit of length. One meter is equal to 1,000 millimeters.

milligram (mg) A metric unit of mass. 1,000 milligrams equal 1 gram.

milliliter (mL) A metric unit of capacity. 1,000 milliliters equal 1 liter.

millimeter (mm) A metric unit of length. 1,000 millimeters equal 1 meter.

mixed number A number that has a whole-number part and a fractional part.

multiple The product of a given whole number and any other whole number.

multiple of 10 A number that has 10 as a factor.

Multiplication Property of Equality Both sides of an equation can be multiplied by the same nonzero number and the sides remain equal.

multiplicative inverse (reciprocal) Two numbers whose product is one.

436

net A plane figure which, when folded, gives the original shape of a solid.

numerator The number above the fraction bar in a fraction.

obtuse angle An angle whose measure is between 90° and 180°.

135°

obtuse triangle A triangle in which one angle is an obtuse angle.

octagon A polygon with 8 sides.

order of operations The order in which operations are done in calculations. Work inside parentheses is done first. Next, terms with exponents are evaluated. Then multiplication and division are done in order from left to right, and finally addition and subtraction are done in order from left to right.

ordered pair A pair of numbers used to locate a point on a coordinate grid.

origin The point where the two axes of a coordinate plane intersect. The origin is represented by the ordered pair (0, 0).

ounce (oz) A customary unit of weight. 16 ounces equal 1 pound.

outlier A value that is much greater or much less than the other values in a data set.

overestimate The result of using larger numbers to estimate a sum or product. The estimate is larger than the actual answer.

P

parallel lines In a plane, lines that never cross and stay the same distance apart.

parallelogram A quadrilateral with both pairs of opposite sides parallel.

partial products Products found by breaking one of two factors into ones, tens, hundreds, and so on, and then multiplying each of these by the other factor.

pentagon A polygon with 5 sides.

perimeter The distance around the outside of any polygon.

perpendicular lines Two lines that intersect to form square corners or right angles.

pint (pt) A customary unit of capacity equal to 2 cups.

place value The position of a digit in a number that is used to determine the value of the digit.
Example: In 5,318, the 3 is in the hundreds place. So, the 3 has a value of 300.

plane An endless flat surface.

437

point An exact location in space.

polygon A closed plane figure made up of line segments.

pound (lb) A customary unit of weight equal to 16 ounces.

power A number that tells how many times the base is used as a factor.
Example: $10^3 = 10 \times 10 \times 10$; 10 is raised to the 3rd power.

prime factorization The process of writing a whole number as a product of its prime factors.

prime number A whole number greater than 1 that has exactly two factors, itself and 1.

prism A solid figure with two congruent parallel bases and faces that are parallelograms.

product The number that is the result of multiplying two or more factors.

proper fraction A fraction less than 1; its numerator is less than its denominator.

protractor An instrument used to measure and draw angles.

pyramid A solid figure with a base that is a polygon and whose faces are triangles with a common vertex.

quadrilateral A polygon with 4 sides.

quart (qt) A customary unit of capacity equal to 2 pints.

quotient The answer to a division problem.

ray Part of a line that has one endpoint and extends forever in one direction.

reciprocal A given number is a reciprocal of another number if the product of the numbers is one.
Example: The numbers $\frac{1}{8}$ and $\frac{8}{1}$ are reciprocals because $\frac{1}{8} \times \frac{8}{1} = 1$.

rectangle A parallelogram with four right angles.

regular polygon A polygon that has sides of equal length and angles of equal measure.

resizing Changing the size of a figure while maintaining the shape of the figure and the measures of its angles.

rhombus A parallelogram with all sides the same length.

right angle An angle whose measure is 90°.

right triangle A triangle in which one angle is a right angle.

rounding A process that determines which multiple of 10, 100, 1,000, etc., a number is closest to.

438

sample A representative part of a larger group.

scale (in a graph) A series of numbers at equal intervals along an axis on a graph.

scalene triangle A triangle in which no sides have the same length.

scaling Multiplying by a number such that the relation of quantities is maintained.

sequence A set of numbers that follows a pattern.

sides (of an angle) The two rays that form an angle.

simplest form A fraction in which the greatest common factor of the numerator and denominator is one.

solid figure (also: solid) A figure that has three dimensions and takes up space.

square A rectangle with all sides the same length.

squared A name for a number to the second power.

standard form A common way of writing a number with commas separating groups of three digits starting from the right. *Example:* 3,458

straight angle An angle measuring 180°.

Subtraction Property of Equality The same number can be subtracted from both sides of an equation and the sides remain equal.

sum The number that is the result of adding two or more addends.

survey A question or questions used to gather information.

table of *x*- and *y*-values A table used to show how *x* and *y* are related.

tenth One out of ten equal parts of a whole.

terms Numbers in a sequence or variables, such as *x* and *y* in an algebraic expression.

thousandth One out of 1,000 equal parts of a whole.

three-dimensional shape A solid with three dimensions that has volume, such as a rectangular prism.

ton (T) A customary unit of weight equal to 2,000 pounds.

trapezoid A quadrilateral that has exactly one pair of parallel sides.

triangle A polygon with 3 sides.

439

underestimate The result of using lesser numbers to estimate a sum or product. The estimate is smaller than the actual answer.

value (of a digit) The number a digit represents, which is determined by the position of the digit. See also *place value*.

variable A letter, such as *n*, that represents a number in an expression or an equation.

vertex (plural: vertices) **a.** The common endpoint of the two rays in an angle. **b.** The point at which three or more edges meet in a solid figure. **c.** The point of a cone.

volume The number of cubic units needed to fill a solid figure.

weight A measure of how light or how heavy something is.

whole numbers The numbers 0, 1, 2, 3, 4, and so on.

word form A way to write a number using words.

x-axis A horizontal line that includes both positive and negative numbers.

x-coordinate The first number in an ordered pair, which names the distance to the right or left from the origin along the *x*-axis.

y-axis A vertical line that includes both positive and negative numbers.

y-coordinate The second number in an ordered pair, which names the distance up or down from the origin along the *y*-axis.

Zero Property of Multiplication The product of any number and 0 is 0.

Credits

Photographs

Every effort has been made to secure permission and provide appropriate credit for photographic material. The publisher deeply regrets any omission and pledges to correct errors called to its attention in subsequent editions.

Unless otherwise acknowledged, all photographs are the property of Scott Foresman, a division of Pearson Education.

Photo locators denoted as follows: Top (T), Center (C), Bottom (B), Left (L), Right (R), Background (Bkgd)

Illustrations
62 Paul Sharp; **62, 118, 119, 125, 131, 151, 165, 170, 172, 175, 227, 290** Rob Schuster; **259** Leslie Kell.

Photographs
Every effort has been made to secure permission and provide appropriate credit for photographic material. The publisher deeply regrets any omission and pledges to correct errors called to its attention in subsequent editions.

Unless otherwise acknowledged, all photographs are the property of Pearson Education, Inc.

Photo locators denoted as follows: Top (T), Center (C), Bottom (B), Left (L), Right (R), Background (Bkgd)

Cover
Luciana Navarro Powell

3 (CL) Michael Legge/Fotolia; **7** (BR) Stockbyte/Thinkstock; **10** (CR) Getty Images/Thinkstock, (BR) Zakharchenko/Fotolia; **14** (TR) Vladislav Gajic/Fotolia; **16** (TR) Getty Images/Hemera Technologies/Thinkstock, (TR) Ivelin Radkov/Fotolia, (TR) James Steidl/Fotolia; **27** (BL) Stockbyte/Getty Images; **48** (TR) ©Robert Marien/Corbis, (TC) ©Royalty-Free/Corbis; **61** (CL) Getty Images/Thinkstock; **69** (BR) Digital Vision/Thinkstock; **89** (L) Richard Carey/Fotolia; **117** (L) Jean-Jacques Cordier/Fotolia; **126** (TR) ©Visions of America. LLC/Alamy; **133** Steve Lovegrove/Fotolia; **143** (BL) ©imagebroker/Alamy; **159** (C) Index Open; **167** (L) jupiterimages/Thinkstock; **173** 2010/Photos to Go/Photolibrary; **175** (BR, BC) Getty Images; **191** (L) 2010/Photos to Go/Photolibrary; **197** Eric Isselée/Fotolia; **219** (Bkgrd) Comstock Images/Jupiter Images; **249** (L) Stephen Meese/Fotolia; **262** (TR) Image Source/Jupiter Images; **273** Getty Images/Jupiterimages/Thinkstock; **329** (L) Alexstar/Fotolia; **332** (TC) Getty Images; **336** (TR) Getty Images; **351** Pascal Thillerot/Fotolia; **354** (TR) Alaskan Express/Jupiter Images; **369** (L) 2010/Photos to Go/Photolibrary; **373** (BR, BL) Jupiter Images; **375** (R) 2010/Photos to Go/Photolibrary; **389** (CL) Fotolia.

▲ **Student Edition**

Index

A

Act It Out strategy, 212–213

Activities. *See Differentiated Instruction, Vocabulary Activities, and Problem-Based Interactive Learning.*

Acute angle, 375

Acute triangle, 375

Addition
Associative Property, 27, 30, 429
Commutative Property, 27, 30, 428
expressions, 204–205
fractions, 219
Identity Property, 429
mixed numbers, 260–261, 264–266
modeling, 256–258
of decimals, 27, 30–32, 40–42, 46–47, 53
to solve problems, 238–239
whole numbers, 3
with unlike denominators, 234–235

Advanced/Gifted, 2I, 27C, 61C, 89C, 117C, 143C, 167C, 191C, 219C, 249C, 273C, 305C, 329C, 351C, 369C, 389C. *See also Close/Assess and Differentiate of each lesson in the Teacher's Edition.*

Algebra Connections
Completing Number Sentences, 101
Completing Tables, 131
Equations with Fractions, 243
Number Patterns, 39
Simplifying Numerical Expressions, 77
Variables, 155

Algebraic expressions, 195, 211, 369
numerical, 191
order of operations, 196–198
simplifying, 77, 200–201
variables in, 194–195

Angles
acute, 375
classifying quadrilaterals by, 380–381
classifying triangles by, 375
measuring and classifying, 375
obtuse, 375
right, 375, 377, 379

Animated Glossary, 6, 14, 64, 66, 68, 70, 72, 92, 150, 194, 197, 210, 222, 226, 230, 232, 234, 252, 294, 308, 314, 354, 356, 372, 374, 376, 383, 393, 412, 414, 417, 426, 428

Area
of a rectangle, 286–287
surface, 286

Art and Math, 319

Assessment
Alternate Assessment, 25, 59, 87, 115, 141, 165, 189, 217, 247, 271, 303, 327, 349, 367, 387, 409
Basic Facts Timed-Tests, 26B–26C
Benchmark Tests, 116A, 218A, 328A, 410A
End-of-Year Test, 410B
Formative Assessments. *See Close/Assess and Differentiate of each lesson in the Teacher's Edition.*
Placement Tests, 26A
Review What You Know! 3, 27, 61, 89, 117, 143, 167, 191, 219, 249, 273, 305, 329, 351, 369, 389
Stop and Practice, 105, 185, 285
Topic Test, 24–25, 58–59, 86–87, 114–115, 140–141, 164–165, 188–189, 216–217, 246–247, 270–271, 302–303, 326–327, 348–349, 366–367, 386–387, 408–409

Associative Property
of Addition, 429
of Multiplication, 429

Associative Property of Addition, 27, 30, 429

Associative Property of Multiplication, 65, 429

Axis
x-, 393–394
y-, 393–394

B

Base, 71
cone, 309
cylinder, 309
parallelograms, 309
prism, 309
pyramid, 309

Below Level, 2I, 27C, 61C, 89C, 117C, 143C, 167C, 191C, 219C, 249C, 273C, 305C, 329C, 351C, 369C, 389C. *See also Close/Assess and Differentiate of each lesson in the Teacher's Edition.*

Benchmark fractions, 227

Billions place, 7

Brackets, order of operations, 202–203

Big Idea, 2G, 27A, 61A, 89A, 117A, 143A, 167A, 191A, 219A, 249A, 273A, 305A, 329A, 351A, 369A, 389A

C

Capacity
customary units, 334–335
metric units, 340–341

Center Activities. *See the last page of each lesson in the Teacher's Edition.*

Centimeter, 338

Charts, place value, 7, 9, 13, 15

Check for Reasonableness strategy, 96–97

Circle graph, 226

Circles, base, 309

Classifying
plane figures, 369
quadrilaterals, 380–381
triangles, 374–375

Index

Index

Notes